identity

DISCOVER DISCIPLESHIP

WORKBOOK 1: DISCOVER IDENTITY

Jay Morgan

All scripture quotations, unless otherwise indicated, are taken from the Holy Bible, New International Version®, NIV®. Copyright ©1973, 1978, 1984, 2011 by Biblica, Inc.TM Used by permission of Zondervan. All rights reserved world- wide. www. zondervan.com The "NIV" and "New International Version" are trademarks registered in the United States Patent and Trademark Office by Biblica, Inc.TM

Scripture quotations marked (NLT) are taken from the Holy Bible, New Living Translation, copyright ©1996, 2004, 2015 by Tyndale House Foundation. Used by permission of Tyndale House Publishers, Inc., Carol Stream, Illinois 60188. All rights reserved.

Scripture quotations marked (NASB) are taken from the New American Standard Bible® Copyright © 1960, 1962, 1963, 1968, 1971, 1972, 1973, 1975, 1977, 1995 by The Lockman Foundation Used by permission. www.Lockman.org
Exterior and Interior design by Jennifer Lam

ISBN 978-1-7337429-2-4

Printed in USA, 2019
10 9 8 7 6 5 4 3 2 1

Published by: River Wild Publishing
PO Box 94
Brenton WV 24818
www.riverwildpublishing.com

table of contents

getting the most from this study

We are glad that you have chosen to pursue this course of study, and hope that you are looking forward to beginning. Before you dig in, there are three important things to take into account:

SMALL DAILY INVESTMENT

To get the maximum benefit from this course of study, a 10-15 minute investment to complete a lesson each day is recommended.

Small choices that we make each day create the lives we live. Your commitment to spending a few minutes each day to think, journal, study and learn, is a commitment to planting and watering seeds of change.

By doing this, you are creating a harvest of good fruit in your life for yourself and for others to benefit from over time. Even if you do not continue this study, forming the habit of taking time for daily personal growth will benefit you for the rest of your life.

WEEKLY DISCUSSION WITH OTHERS

Each journey that we take in life, whether physical or material, is more enjoyable when we have companions. Someone may see something that you missed, or have an idea that is different than your own. Travel is almost always safer in groups.

Likewise, we encourage you to meet regularly with another person or a group of people to discuss your thoughts. Spend time with someone who is farther down the spiritual road so that you can learn from and lean on them as you progress along your own path. This road is too serious for you to travel upon alone.

MORE THAN A STUDY

This workbook is the first in a series of six. You will find that the six core discoveries as put forth in this series will serve you well beyond this study. These core discoveries are to be used as guides for your spiritual journey, and the workbooks will serve as reference guides throughout your lifetime. The content doesn't end with the course.

Also, keep in mind that each of the six workbooks in this series builds upon each other. It is imperative that you study them in order—and completely—to get the most out of this study.

May God bless you as you increase in your knowledge of Him.

Pastor Jay Morgan

group guidelines

If you are completing this Study in a group setting, the following guidelines will help keep meetings safe, focused and productive:

1. **I will commit to making the group meetings and this study a priority by being prepared and being on time.** The group meeting is not the time to work on answers to questions. I understand the group meeting will be unproductive if I have not read the lessons and answered the questions before the group meeting.

2. **I will maintain confidentiality.** What is said in the group stays in the group unless someone threatens to hurt themselves or others. In that case, appropriate people will be notified to ensure the safety of all parties involved.

3. **I will refrain from gossiping about others during the group meeting.** I will keep my focus on my experiences and not on other people. I will leave others' names anonymous when sharing my negative personal experiences in the group setting

4. **I will be honest.** The purpose of this Study is to give honest answers and work toward the study of God's truth. Everyone is here to discover God's truth together. We cannot discover truth until we ask questions and seek answers.

5. **I will respect the other members of the group.** I will refrain from being on electronic devices, interrupting others and/or having side conversations.

6. **I understand that my role is not to "save" or "fix" anyone else.** Together, our role is to continue to point each other toward Jesus and the truth of His teachings.

notes

....
....
....
....
....
....
....
....
....
....
....
....
....
....
....
....
....
....
....
....
....

introduction to identity

> The two most important days in your life are the day you are born and the day you find out why. **— AUTHOR UNKNOWN**

why are you here?

Scholars study. Philosophers contemplate. Poets wonder. Scientists analyze.

We all want to know if there is a reason for our existence. You too, have probably wondered if your life has meaning; if it does, how can you find it?

It is natural to want to know why you are here. The search for the meaning of life is hard-wired into our DNA. Whether or not you realize it, that quest drives most of your decisions and actions.[1]

This drive to search for meaning is in us so that we will not just *search* for meaning, but find it. The truth is: *you were created for greatness.*

THE MEANING OF LIFE

The Bible offers an intriguing explanation for the meaning of life: God, an uncontainable Spirit who is larger than the universe, created *everything*—including *you*—for a reason. In other words, the universe is not the result of a random string of events. There is a design and a purpose behind it all.

> By wisdom the LORD laid the earth's foundations, by understanding he set the heavens in place. —**Proverbs 3:19**

> ... all things have been created through him and for him. —**Colossians 1:16b**

So, if God had a plan and created everything for a purpose, where does humanity fit? What is the reason for human life? Why did He create *us?*

Scripture answers this by revealing that God made humanity in His image. God calls us His children. He crowns us with glory and honor.

> Then God said, "Let us make mankind in our image, in our likeness..." —**Genesis 1:26a**

> ...Adam, the son of God. —**Luke 3:38b**

> What is mankind that you are mindful of them, human beings that you care for them? You have made them a little lower than the angels and crowned them with glory and honor.
> —**Psalm 8:4-5**

The answer to the question, "Why am I here?" is found only by discovering *who you are.*

You are a child of God.

Up to this point in life, you have probably identified yourself by things you do or by roles you have assumed.

1. **In what ways have you defined yourself in the past? Circle all that apply:**

By relationships: I am a father or mother. I am an aunt or uncle. I am a grandparent. A husband or wife. A son or daughter. Other:

By occupation: I am a teacher. A boss. A housewife. I am a nurse or doctor. A secretary, a waitress, a custodian. I am an entrepreneur. A student. Other:

By a label: I am a success, or a failure. I am good, bad, rich, poor, pretty, ugly, thin, fat, smart, dumb. Other:

By pain: I am an addict, alcoholic, anorexic. I am an abuser. I am a victim. I am a felon. I am divorced. Other:

These things are not *who* you *are*. These are *roles* which you have assumed in life and these roles rarely remain constant.

For some people, this is good news. Knowing that they do not need to live out negative identities they have developed can free them.

On the other hand, some people have worked a lifetime to develop their identity through their roles. The thought of losing what they have created can be alarming.

2. Is it good news or bad news for you that the roles you have assumed do not truly define who you are? Why?

your created identity

Being made as a child of God–in the image of God–means that you are designed to live life in a certain way. Everything functions best when it functions within its intended design.[2]

You are designed to share life with God. It is evident while reading the opening pages of Scripture in Genesis, that God desires to both give love to and receive love from us, His children. The first humans experienced a very personal relationship with God. He walked, talked and interacted with them.

The Christian church has an old statement of belief: "Man's chief end (reason for existence) is to glorify God and enjoy Him forever."[3] You were made to bring glory to God and you were made to enjoy God.

Remember:

> ... all things have been created through him and
> for him. —**Colossians 1:16b**

You are designed to partner with God on a meaningful mission. As image-bearers of God, we have the ability to reason, think, create and adapt. We are given the mandate and authority to rule over and subdue (govern) the earth. This means we are called to bring God's authority, care, and order to the entire earth. No other creation was given this responsibility, because no other creation was made in the image of God.

> Then God said, "Let us make mankind in our
> image, in our likeness, so that they may rule
> over the fish in the sea and the birds in the sky,
> over the livestock and all the wild animals,
> and over all the creatures that move along the
> ground." —**Genesis 1:26** *(Emphasis added)*

You are designed to share life with others. Although Adam, the first man, enjoyed God's Presence and had a meaningful purpose for living, he still desired companionship. God said that it is not good for man to be alone, so He made Eve.

> The LORD God said, "It is not good for the man
> to be alone. I will make a helper suitable for
> him." —**Genesis 2:18**

Notice the word that God used to describe Eve: she would be a helper. Humans were made to help each other to fulfill our God given mission in the world. God blessed them and gave them the shared responsibility of ruling over the world together.

> God blessed *them* and said to *them*, "Be fruitful
> and increase in number; fill the earth and
> subdue it. Rule over the fish in the sea and the
> birds in the sky and over every living creature
> that moves on the ground." —**Genesis 1:28**
> *(Emphasis added)*

In the same way that a loving father might show his children his vast estate and then proudly say, "All of this is yours to enjoy, so take care of it and take care of each other," God placed His children in charge of this world.

God did not create humanity because He was helpless without us. God created us in His image because He desires to have a family with which to share His love and blessings. God wants us to enjoy Him, each other, and have meaningful purpose for eternity.

God created *you* because He *desires* to share life with you—as your Father. He *desires* for you to share life with Him as His child.

1. **What is your reaction to the truth that God created you because He desires to have a family to share eternity with?**

lost identity

The Bible teaches us that the first humans experienced a meaningful relationship with God as His children. Their lives had true meaning because they lived within their *created design* of loving God, loving each other, and bringing God's rule to the world.

However, a tree with forbidden fruit was in the Garden.

> And the LORD God commanded the man,
> "You are free to eat from any tree in the garden;
> but you must not eat from the tree of the
> knowledge of good and evil, for when you eat
> from it you will certainly die."
> —**Genesis 2:16-17**

And God had an enemy—Satan.

Satan began his existence as a musical cherub, or an angel, named Lucifer. He was proud and wanted to *be* God. Lucifer, along with other rebellious angels, led a revolt in Heaven. As a result, one-third of God's created angels were cast down to earth and into Hell to await their final judgment (Isaiah 14:12-17; Revelation 12:3-10; Luke 10:18).

While on earth, in the form of a serpent, Satan seduced Eve and then Adam to disobey and betray God. He deceived God's beloved family into sharing his fate—eternal separation from God. He lured them away from God and from their created design.

> Now the serpent was craftier than any of the
> wild animals the Lord God had made. He said
> to the woman, "Did God really say, 'You must
> not eat from any tree in the garden'?"

> The woman said to the serpent, "We may eat fruit from the trees in the garden, but God did say, 'You must not eat fruit from the tree that is in the middle of the garden, and you must not touch it, or you will die.'"
>
> "You will not certainly die," the serpent said to the woman. "For God knows that when you eat from it your eyes will be opened, and you will be like God, knowing good and evil."
> —**Genesis 3:1-5**

Satan placed doubts in their hearts about God's goodness.

- He convinced them that they could not trust God.

- He convinced them that they should be in control and that they should decide for themselves what is right or wrong—not God.

- He convinced them that meaning was found apart from God.

- He convinced them that they could pursue what they wanted—self-gratification— without consequences.

Sound familiar?

THE CONSEQUENCES OF SIN

Adam and Eve listened to those lies and decided to act upon them. They disobeyed God and ate from the forbidden tree.

Just as God had warned, they experienced death because of their sin. Their spiritual identity as God's children was destroyed through their separation from Him. This spiritual death soon led to death in every part of their lives. Life fueled by God's love and living for their created design was destroyed. (You can read more about this in Genesis 3:1-24.)

- Their distrust of God separated them from Him and severed the relationship with Him they were designed for. They hid from God and covered themselves to hide their shame.

- Their distrust of God not only separated them from God, it also destroyed the unity they shared with each other. Adam immediately blamed Eve for his choices. The shared companionship they had enjoyed was replaced with a struggle for power and dominance which quickly led to humans murdering and exploiting each other for their own gain, beginning with one of their sons murdering the other.

- The meaningful mission of being image-bearers of God and bringing God's rule and authority to the world was replaced by a curse. The world would work against them. Their survival now depended upon pain and labor.

Because you were made *for* God and designed to live as His child, living your life for anything else will only lead to disappointment. The search for meaning is not wrong. However, searching for meaning outside of God is ultimately useless and destructive.

1. **Would you describe yourself as close to God or separated from Him? Why?**

LOVE REQUIRES A CHOICE

Many wonder why God placed the tree in the garden in the first place. Why did God create an opportunity for disobedience?

We must realize that God did not create us to be His "puppets." What God desires most from us is a love-based relationship. True love is not forced or coerced; it is based on choice. If someone is forced to love you, is it really love?

God wants us to choose Him because we *want* to choose Him, not because we *have* to choose Him.

This means that for you to truly make a choice to love God, you must also have the choice to not love God. In order to choose to trust and obey God, the choice to disobey God must be present.

2. **Do you agree that love must be based on a choice? Why or why not?**

notes

the search for identity

> "But as I looked at everything I had worked so hard to accomplish, it was all so meaningless—like chasing the wind. There was nothing really worthwhile anywhere."
>
> — ECCLESIASTES 2:11 NLT

substitute identities

The search for meaning is usually driven by seeking the satisfaction of the following three basic needs: [4]

The need for security. We all have a core instinct for survival. Security is the confidence that your present and future needs are met. It is confidence that you can survive in this world.

The need for worth. Because we were created in the image of God and crowned with glory and honor, we have a need to feel that our lives matter—that we have worth.

The need for fulfillment. As image bearers of God, we desire to have purpose. We know that we were created for more than just existence, and we remain restless until we discover our created design.

As a loving Father, God created a perfect world for His children. Adam and Eve were secure in God's provision. They were crowned with glory (worth) and honor. Fulfillment was found by walking with God and living in their created design.

SUBSTITUTE IDENTITIES

When Adam and Eve were separated from God through their sin, they no longer found their security, worth and fulfillment through their identity as His children. But these basic needs did not simply disappear. They still exist inside all of us.

If these basic needs are not satisfied through our created design as God's children, we seek satisfaction from other sources.

We create new, *substitute identities* based on things, other people, and/or ourselves. (Refer to the list on page 15. For a list with related Scriptures, refer to *Appendix I*).[5]

SUBSTITUTE IDENTITIES LIST

ACCOMPLISHMENTS	I am defined by what I can do or by what I know.
ABILITIES	I am defined by a skill or ability that I have.
POSSESSIONS	I am defined by what I own.
APPEARANCE	I am defined by how I look.
APPROVAL	I am defined by who accepts me.
ATTENTION	I am defined by being noticed for positive or negative behavior, or by getting sympathy from others.
POWER	I am defined by being in control.
AFFECTION	I am defined by who loves me.
APPETITES	I am defined by my desires. These can be natural desires such as those of food or sex, or acquired desires such as those for drugs or alcohol.
PLEASURE	I am defined by feeling good.

When we think about it, looking to something other than God to meet our needs is what leads to sin in the first place. We look to an object, a person or ourselves to give us what only He can provide.

These substitutes can feel authentic because they deliver a temporary sense of security, worth or fulfillment; but it is just an illusion. These substitutes demand increasingly more from us and are never satisfied.

The search for security, worth and fulfillment apart from God has brought pain and chaos into the world since the moment of Adam and Eve's betrayal.

Because we were made in God's image, nothing else can truly substitute for our true identity as His children. Nothing else can truly meet our needs.

However, when you understand and live for your created design as a child of God, you are secure because of Him. You understand your worth as God's child. You find fulfillment through God's love and your created design.

Reflect on the following statement:

> *Because I am a child of God made in His image, I will only find true security, worth, and fulfillment by accepting His love and living in my created design as His child.*

1. **In what ways would your life be different if you lived this truth?**

the search for security

Security is the confidence that your present and future needs are met. It is confidence that you can continue to survive in this world.

Security has been described as a fundamental human need, along the same lines as needing food.

Substitute Identities cause us to rely upon an object, other people, or ourselves for a sense of security.

For example, to make themselves feel secure, some rely on their abilities or power to provide for their needs. Others find security by relying on someone else's power or ability to provide.

Owning possessions such as a house, a car, or even idol gods brings security to some. For others, appearance makes them feel secure because they see it as a means to get what they need from people.

1. Review the Substitute Identities list on page 15. Which of these have made you feel safe or secure?

2. Indicate the source of the security you find through these Substitute Identities. Is it an object, another person, or yourself that makes you feel secure?

A feeling of security does not necessarily mean you are actually safe. It means you have the *perception* of safety.

We often find security in what is familiar, even if it hurts us. Sadly, people will go to great lengths and suffer significant pain to continue a bad habit or maintain a destructive relationship that is familiar. Change seems too risky.

3. **Describe ways in which you have tolerated an unhealthy situation because changing, leaving or losing it seemed too risky.**

FINDING SECURITY

Jesus taught a level of security that only comes from complete reliance on God.

> So do not worry, saying, "What shall we eat?" or "What shall we drink?" or "What shall we wear?" For the pagans run after all these things, and your heavenly Father knows that you need them. But seek first his kingdom and his righteousness, and all these things will be given to you as well. Therefore do not worry about tomorrow, for tomorrow will worry about itself. Each day has enough trouble of its own.
> —Matthew 6:31-34

4. **Have you ever looked to God as your source of security? Why or why not?**

The Security Lie:
I cannot trust God; He withholds good from me.

The Truth About Security:
Because I am a child of God made in His image, I will only find
true security by accepting His love and by living in my created
design as His child.

As a child of God you do not have to look to others or yourself to
"fix" everything. You can relax and be secure in your role as His
child. Your responsibilities as God's child are to listen to Him, trust
Him and obey Him. When you do this, you can trust Him with
the outcomes.

5. **What does it mean to listen to and obey God, and then
    trust Him with the outcomes?**

6. **In what ways would your life be different if you lived
    the truth about security?**

the search for worth

Because we are created in the image of God and crowned with glory and honor, we have a need to feel that our lives matter—that we have worth.

What do you value? It is critically important to know the answer to this question.

If you possess what you value, you feel that you have value or worth. If you do not possess what you value, you feel worthless.

For example, if you think that a certain person has value, your feelings of value and worth increase if they notice you or give you affection.

If you value the power, pleasure or attention you get from owning things, then you feel that your value increases with owning more.

If you value appearance, your self-worth is based upon how you look.

1. **Review the Substitute Identities list on page 15. To which of these have you assigned value?**

2. **What is the source of this value? An object, other people, or yourself?**

FINDING WORTH

To find your true worth, you need to change the things that you value.

Things of this world are temporary. They do not last. They demand increasingly more from you. They promise bigger, better, brighter—but leave you empty.

What is truly valuable?

God.

If you have God, you have what is most precious in the universe. Nothing compares to Him. Not an object, emotion, relationship or opinion can come close to the treasure of Heaven in your life. When you have the Source of all value, you have value.

Notice how Apostle Paul, one of Jesus' early followers, changed his source of value and worth. Before encountering Jesus, Paul lived his life pursuing worth from a variety of Substitute Identities.

Paul was proud that he was born into the "right" family, religion and nation. He excelled at everything he set out to accomplish. He had tremendous power and influence. When Paul encountered the reality of Who Jesus is, he gave up everything that was of value to him. This is his reaction:

> I once thought these things were valuable,
> but now I consider them worthless because
> of what Christ has done. Yes, everything else
> is worthless when compared with the infinite
> value of knowing Christ Jesus my Lord. For his
> sake I have discarded everything else, counting
> it all as garbage, so that I could gain Christ.
> —**Philippians 3:7-8 NLT**

3. Have you ever viewed God as your source of worth? Why or why not?

The Worth Lie:
Value (worth) can be found apart from God.

The Truth About Worth:
Because I am a child of God made in His image, I will only find true worth by accepting His love and by living in my created design as His child.

As a child of God, you were created to have a relationship with Him. If you have Him, you have unsurpassed worth. What others think of you no longer defines you because you know He loves you.

4. What does it mean to say, "If I have God, I have unsurpassed worth"?

5. In what ways would your life be different if you lived the truth about worth?

the search
for fulfillment

Fulfillment is defined as a feeling of completeness and satisfaction. It can also be described as being at peace or content.

As image bearers of God, we desire purpose. We have an inherent sense that we were created for more than just existence. We remain restless until we discover and live in our created design as children of God.

There are many ways that we look to Substitute Identities to provide fulfillment and settle our restlessness.

Many people believe that they will find fulfillment through self-gratification. In other words they think that if they can gratify their desires and whims, they will find peace and contentment.

Others seek fulfillment through personal accomplishments. Some pursue fulfillment from attention and affection they get from a person.

Some find fulfillment through what they own, while others are pleasure-seekers.

1. **Review the Substitute Identities list on page 15. In what ways have you sought fulfillment through any these means?**

2. **What is the source of this fulfillment? An object, other people, or yourself?**

FINDING FULFILLMENT

Notice the way in which believers in God and His Son Jesus have described finding fulfillment in life:

> As the deer pants for streams of water, so my soul pants for you, my God. My soul thirsts for God, for the living God. When can I go and meet with God? —**King David in Psalm 42**

> ...I have learned to be content whatever the circumstances. I know what it is to have plenty. I have learned the secret of being content in any and every situation, whether well-fed or hungry, whether living in plenty or in want. I can do everything through him who gives me strength. —**Apostle Paul in Philippians 4**

> You have made us for yourself, and our heart is restless until it finds its rest in you.
> —**St. Augustine**

These men experienced an intense desire for intimacy with God that goes far beyond the rituals of religion. They describe a vibrant relationship with God as the real source of fulfillment in their lives.

3. **In what ways does this intense desire for God differ from the opinion of God or religion that you hold?**

Jesus described a relationship with God as drinking from a well that never runs dry. When He said this, He was speaking with a woman who lived a noticeably unfulfilled life. She had been in several failed relationships and was in another dysfunctional one.

> ...whoever drinks the water I give them will never thirst. Indeed, the water I give them will become in them a spring of water welling up to eternal life. —**John 4:14b**

Jesus made her aware that there is a fulfillment that does not depend on other people, external circumstances, or self-gratification, but springs up from within a person.

The Fulfillment Lie:
Fulfillment comes apart from God; I know what is best for me.

The Truth About Fulfillment:
Because I am a child of God made in His image, I will only find true fulfillment in His love and by living in my created design as His child.

As a child of God, His love fills and fulfills you. You are free from the drive to pursue empty, Substitute Identities. You can "drink" from His love and purpose, and be satisfied.

4. **What does it mean to be fulfilled by God's love?**

5. **In what ways would your life be different if you lived the Truth about fulfillment?**

why substitute identities fall short

When you seek your identity from false sources, you seek meaning apart from your relationship with God. You rely upon things, other people and/or yourself to provide security, worth and fulfillment.

VALIDATION FROM THINGS

This form of validation plays out in different ways. It can be as extreme as outright worship of idols, or as subtle as materialism. Either way, you look to an object—not God—to provide a sense of security, worth and/or fulfillment.

Most people do not realize the level that they depend upon material things to meet their core desires.

On some level, we all use material objects, but seeing them as our source of validation is dangerous. The problem with material objects is that they are temporal—this means they are temporary. They do not last. If your validation is attached to them, your sense of identity is lost when those things are gone.

> Do not store up for yourselves treasures on earth, where moths and vermin destroy, and where thieves break in and steal. But store up for yourselves treasures in heaven, where moths and vermin do not destroy, and where thieves do not break in and steal.
> —Matthew 6:19-20

1. In what ways has losing an object (theft, bankruptcy, misplacement, etc.) or having an object destroyed (flood, fire, natural disaster, vandalism, etc.) made you feel insecure, worthless or empty?

VALIDATION FROM OTHER PEOPLE

Review the Substitute Identities list. Notice how many of them rely upon human opinion. We allow the attention, approval and affection of others to dictate what we think and how we feel about ourselves. Trying to influence other people's opinion of us is often why we obsess about our possessions, appearance and accomplishments. Other times we completely depend upon what another person possesses or does to provide us with a sense of security, worth or fulfillment.

2. In what ways have you allowed other people's opinions to influence how you feel about yourself?

We have an innate desire for companionship with others; as a result, human relationships play a vital role in life. However, centering your life solely on any human relationship—no matter how healthy—is risky.

The truth is that all human relationships end. Relationships do not always end in negative ways, but they do end. People move and lose contact. Friends enter different stages of life and have new responsibilities and less in common. Sometimes betrayal destroys a relationship. Eventually, death separates us all.

If you base your identity on a human relationship, you will believe that you have no purpose when that relationship is gone.

3. **In what ways has an ended relationship caused you to feel insecure, worthless or empty?**

VALIDATION FROM YOURSELF

Although many people look to others for validation, some look to themselves. They try to create a positive self-image. They become self-reliant. They find a sense of security, worth and fulfillment by succeeding in life or through their looks or abilities. Some go as far as to live completely for themselves with no regard for others. Getting or doing what they want is all that matters.

Although it is good to feel grateful that you are uniquely created and gifted, this cannot be your source of validation. Every substitute identity is temporary and has no lasting guarantee or value.

Health, abilities and looks fade. Opportunities are lost and the thrill of personal accomplishments loses appeal. If you attach your identity to these things, you will be left feeling insecure, worthless, and empty when life changes.

4. In what ways has losing an opportunity or failing in a Substitute Identity made you feel insecure, worthless or empty?

TRUE VALIDATION

When your validation is based on God and your identity as His child, your source of meaning will remain constant.

> I the Lord do not change… —**Malachi 3:6**

You do not need to be defined by your roles or by any earthly attachment. God has made it possible for you to find and live in your true identity as His child.

Everything that you have searched for in life can be found in God's love. You no longer need to settle for empty, Substitute Identities. You can find it in your true identity.

> And I am convinced that nothing can ever separate us from God's love. Neither death nor life, neither angels nor demons, neither our fears for today nor our worries about tomorrow—not even the powers of hell can separate us from God's love.
>
> No power in the sky above or in the earth below—indeed, nothing in all creation will ever be able to separate us from the love of God that is revealed in Christ Jesus our Lord.
> —**Romans 8:38-39 NLT**

reactions to spiritual searching

It is easy to follow the pattern of everyone around you and to continue the search for your identity through substitutes. Rather than bringing meaning that lasts, these Substitute Identities demand increasingly more.

The search for meaning, security, worth and fulfillment outside of God leaves a hole that can never be filled. King Solomon, the wisest man who ever lived, called it "chasing the wind."[6]

It may seem as if what you search for is always within reach, but you can never grab hold of it. While you run toward so many things you think you want, you are actually running away from God. You end up feeling empty; the emptiness is because you are separated from God.

Jesus referred to this state as being *lost*.[7]

WHY DO SO MANY PEOPLE REMAIN LOST?

Some are unaware that they are lost and searching. It often takes a tragic life event, such as betrayal or the death of a loved one, to wake them up and motivate them to actively seek real answers.

1. What has caused you to think about spiritual matters?

Many choose to numb their souls while searching. Some people cannot handle the emptiness and pain of being spiritually lost. They try to ignore it or numb themselves through drug and alcohol use or abuse. Or they stay busy, burying themselves in Substitute Identities.

2. In what ways have you attempted to ignore or numb your soul to emptiness and pain?

Most repeat the same fruitless search. Although they may realize that the ways they search for meaning leave them empty, people still keep trying to fill the hole left in their lives by substitutes. They seem to believe that if they can run the chase out a little further they will be happy.

Someone who seeks their identity through affection or attention may pursue relationship after relationship. They always believe that the next one will fill that empty place.

People who believe that their identity can be found in possessions will buy things. As the "new" wears off, they want bigger and better.

Those who look toward accomplishments for their identity are never satisfied for long; they are not happy with what they have achieved.

Someone whose self-worth is based on their appearance can never look good enough.

When one source fails, there is always another. If relationships are not working, a disappointed person may overachieve, or buy more toys, or get a makeover. When feelings of failure take over, some turn to over-indulgence and develop substance, sex and/or food addictions. You get the picture.

Self-gratification will never bring soul satisfaction. No matter how long you try or how many desires you pursue you will still feel empty, worthless and afraid.

When you find yourself on an endless, fruitless search for meaning, remember this:

Insanity is doing the same thing over and over again and expecting different results.

Maybe it is time to consider a different path.

3. **In what ways have you traded one Substitute Identity for another, or tried to chase one further in the hope of finding satisfaction?**

WHAT BEING A CHILD OF GOD BRINGS

Reflect upon the following identity statements:

Security: As a child of God I understand that I do not need to look to others or myself to "fix" everything. I can relax and be secure in my role as His child. My responsibilities as God's child are to listen to Him, obey Him and trust Him with the outcomes.

Worth: As a child of God, I understand that I was created to have a relationship with Him. If I have Him, I have unsurpassed worth. What others think of me no longer defines me because my worth is found in God's love.

Fulfillment: As a child of God, I understand that His love fills and fulfills me. I am free from the drive to pursue empty, Substitute Identities. I can "drink" from His love and purpose and be satisfied.

4. **Which of these three statements bears the most meaning for your life? Why?**

To fully understand the implications of being a child of God, you must realize that if every role you have assumed in life was stripped away, if every relationship ended that you have enjoyed, if everything you thought important was gone—it would not change *who you are*. God is still your Father and you are still His child. Because of Who He is and your identity in Him, you still have hope, a future, and a purpose. Even if death claims your body, you do not need to fear, because you will be with Him forever.

5. **Go back and underline the parts of the previous paragraph that impact you the most. How would your life be different if you lived these truths?**

the result of life apart from God

In order to fully understand the significance of being a child of God, you must realize the result of living life apart from Him. Substitute Identities might give short-term benefits, but they will not ultimately give what they promise. They lead to destructive (sinful) behaviors.[8]

Some things that become Substitute Identities are not in and of themselves wrong. For example, you may own possessions, receive and give affection, accomplish things, and have great abilities. However, allowing them to define who you are—or pursuing them rather than pursuing God—will lead you into sin and further from your created design as a child of God.

For example, if you believe that your worth is based on the affection or attention you get from others, it can easily lead to the sin of sexual immorality.

If power makes you feel secure, you may use the sins of anger and deception to maintain control.

If you find fulfillment through your accomplishments and abilities, it is easy to succumb to the sin of jealousy of other people's accomplishments and abilities.

A good definition of sin is "to miss the mark."[9] We have all missed the mark and fallen short of God's intended glory.

Through sinful pursuits to find meaning, you have hurt God, others and yourself. Other people have hurt you in their sinful pursuits.

We must realize that when God tells us *no*, it is for a reason. Sin *always* brings pain and death.

For the wages of sin is death... —**Romans 6:23a**

1. Review the Substitute Identities list. Describe a way
    that you have hurt yourself by pursuing one of these.

2. Describe a way you have hurt others by pursuing one
    of these.

3. Describe a way you have been hurt by others in their
    pursuit of one of these.

4. Describe a way that you have separated yourself from God by pursuing one of these.

THE UGLY TRUTH ABOUT SIN

Everyone has sinned and gone his or her own way, away from God. We are all in the same boat. We are all guilty of sin. It does not matter what our sins are; they have led us away from God.

> We all, like sheep, have gone astray, each of us has turned to our own way... —**Isaiah 53:6**

Sin causes you to fall short of God's glory. We are all guilty. Who you are and the "size" of your sin does not matter. Because you have sinned, you have fallen short of the glory of God and the glory you were created for. You have missed the mark.

> For all have sinned and fall short of the glory of God. —**Romans 3:23**

Sin makes you an enemy of God. While most people do not view themselves as God's enemy, sin makes us God's enemy because sinful behavior opposes or fights against what is good and right—God's will and desires.

> Once you were alienated from God and were enemies in your minds because of your evil behavior. —**Colossians 1:21**

Sin makes you a slave. You cannot free yourself from the power (control) of sin. No matter how hard you resist, sin enslaves you.

> Jesus replied, "Very truly I tell you, everyone who sins is a slave to sin." **—John 8:34**

Sin kills. The outcome of sin is death. God warned Adam and Eve—they would die the day that they ate from the Tree of the Knowledge of Good and Evil. They did not physically die that day; they experienced spiritual death through separation from God. The same is true for all of humanity. Because you sin, you are spiritually dead.

> But from the tree of the knowledge of good and evil you shall not eat, for in the day that you eat from it you will surely die.
> **—Genesis 2:17 NASB**

> For the wages of sin is death... **—Romans 3:23**

> As for you, you were dead in your transgressions and sins. **—Ephesians 2:1**

Sin will result in eternal separation from God. Your sin has separated you from God and has brought spiritual death. Spiritual death will result in eternal death. Eternal death is Hell. Hell is eternal separation from God.

Most people are very uncomfortable with the concept of Hell. Because a thought is uncomfortable, inconvenient or unpopular does not mean it is not true. No matter how much you want to avoid this truth—and no matter how unfair you think it is—*spiritual death will bring eternal death in Hell.*

People often wonder how a God of love could send people to Hell. First, realize that Hell was not created for people. It was created for Satan. Hell is Satan's fate.

> Then he will say to those on his left, "Depart
> from me, you who are cursed, into the eternal
> fire prepared for the devil and his angels."
> —**Matthew 25:41**

By luring you away from God and into spiritual death, Satan has caused you to share in his fate. God's will does not send us to Hell; spiritual death that results from sin sends us to Hell. This is why God warns us against sin. He understands the outcome.

> It's your sins that have cut you off from God.
> Because of your sins, he has turned away and
> will not listen anymore. —**Isaiah 59:2 NLT**

> For the wages of sin is death, but the gift of God
> is eternal life in Christ Jesus our Lord.
> —**Romans 6:23**

Sin brings death, but God desires to give you life.

5. **What is your reaction to the truth about sin?**

the Good News of Jesus

"For God so loved the world that he gave his one and only Son, that whoever believes in him shall not perish but have eternal life. —JOHN 3:16"

who is Jesus?

Although sin destroys you and separates you from God, He still loves you and desires an intimate relationship with you. He longs to restore your identity as His child.

Motivated by love, God came through Christ to rescue humanity from spiritual death and eternal separation from Him.

> But God demonstrates his own love for us in this: While we were still sinners, Christ died for us. —**Romans 5:8**

Through faith in Jesus, your identity as a child of God can be restored. This is the Good News— the Gospel—of Jesus.

> Yet to all who did receive him, to those who believed in his name, he gave the right to become children of God. —**John 1:12**

> See what great love the Father has lavished on us, that we should be called children of God! And that is what we are! —**1 John 3:1a NLT**

UNDERSTANDING JESUS' UNIQUE ROLE

To truly understand how faith in Jesus can save you and restore you to God, you must recognize who He really is.

The following excerpt from the Nicene Creed–an ancient statement of beliefs of the Christian faith–summarizes the Biblical teaching on Who Jesus is.

> *We believe in one Lord, Jesus Christ, the only Son of God, eternally begotten of the Father (John 3:16), God from God, Light from Light, true God from true God, begotten, not made, of one Being with the Father. Through Him all things were made (John 1:1-14).*

For us and for our salvation He came down from heaven; by the power of the Holy Spirit He became incarnate from the Virgin Mary (Luke 1:35) and was made man (John 1:14).

For our sake He was crucified under Pontius Pilate; He suffered death and was buried (Matthew 27). On the third day He rose again in accordance with the Scriptures (Matthew 28); He ascended into heaven and is seated at the right hand of the Father (Acts 1:1-11; Ephesians 1:20).

He will come again in glory to judge the living and the dead, and His kingdom will have no end (Acts 1:11; Luke 1:32-33).[10]

Jesus has divine nature. Jesus has eternally existed as the Word of God. He is part of God. This means He has divine (God) nature.

> In the beginning was the Word, and the Word was *with* God, and the Word *was* God.
> —**John 1:1** *(Emphasis added)*

Scripture teaches that all things were created through Jesus and for Jesus; He holds everything together. Scripture also teaches that God created all things (Genesis 1:1). If Jesus is not divine, then this would be a contradiction.

> For in him all things were created: things in heaven and on earth, visible and invisible, whether thrones or powers or rulers or authorities; all things have been created through him and for him. He is before all things, and in him all things hold together.
> —**Colossians 1:16-17**

> For from him and through him and for him are all things. To him be the glory forever! Amen. —**Romans 11:36**

While on earth, Jesus received worship, and He receives worship in Heaven. If He is not God then this would be idolatry—false worship. A practice strictly forbidden in Scripture.

> Suddenly Jesus met them. "Greetings," he said. They came to him, clasped his feet and worshiped him. —**Matthew 28:9**

> In a loud voice they were saying: *"Worthy is the Lamb, who was slain, to receive power and wealth and wisdom and strength and honor and glory and praise!"* Then I heard every creature in heaven and on earth and under the earth and on the sea, and all that is in them, saying: "To him who sits on the throne and *to the Lamb be praise and honor and glory and power, for ever and ever!"* —**Revelations 5:12-13** *(Emphasis added)*

Jesus has human nature. When Jesus was conceived and born into the world, He took on human nature. By taking on human nature, He became God with us. (Immanuel)

> The Word became flesh and made his dwelling among us. We have seen his glory, the glory of the one and only Son, who came from the Father, full of grace and truth. —**John 1:14**

> The virgin will conceive and give birth to a son, and they will call him Immanuel (which means "God with us".) —**Matthew 1:23**

He became the part of God that humanity could see and interact with. He became a visible reference point of God. He became touchable.

> The Son is the image of the invisible God, the firstborn over all creation. —**Colossians 1:15**

> The Son is the radiance of God's glory and the exact representation of his being, sustaining all things by his powerful word. —**Hebrews 1:3a**

Then he (Jesus) said to Thomas, "Put your finger here; see my hands. Reach out your hand and put it into my side. Stop doubting and believe." Thomas said to him, "*My Lord and my God!*" —**John 20:27-28** (*Emphasis added*)

Jesus is both human and divine. This can be a difficult concept to comprehend, but it is critical to understanding the full implications of who Jesus is and what God accomplished through Him.

This unique combination of being both God and man put Him in the position to be the only One who could bridge the gap—mediate— between God and mankind.

For there is one God and one mediator between God and mankind, the man Christ Jesus, who gave himself as a ransom for all people. This has now been witnessed to at the proper time. —**1 Timothy 2:5-6**

So here are the implications: God witnessed His creation, His *children*, leave Him and join His enemy. He knew His children would suffer the same fate as Satan—eternal separation from Him in Hell. God knew we could not save ourselves. So, through Jesus, He clothed Himself in flesh and came to us to rescue us.

1. **Describe your reaction to the truth that God loves you enough to come and rescue you.**

the importance of Jesus' life and teachings

When considering the importance of Jesus to humanity, people often skip straight to His death and resurrection. Although His death and resurrection were necessary to fulfill His mission, His *life and teachings* were also essential to His mission.

Jesus' overarching mission was to destroy the works of the devil and to bring the Kingdom of God—God's will and reign—to earth.

> The one who does what is sinful is of the devil, because the devil has been sinning from the beginning. *The reason the Son of God appeared was to destroy the devil's work. No one who is born of God will continue to sin, because God's seed remains in them; they cannot go on sinning, because they have been born of God.* —**1 John 3:8-9** *(Emphasis added)*

One way that Jesus destroys the devil's work in the world is by teaching us what the will of the Father—the Kingdom of God—truly is.   The truth of God's Word exposes the lies that the devil uses to deceive humanity.

> But he said, "I must proclaim the good news of the kingdom of God to the other towns also, because *that is why I was sent.*" —**Luke 4:43** *(Emphasis added)*

Jesus' life and teachings serve as our example. Jesus' death and resurrection made it possible for us to be forgiven and reborn, but His life and teachings show us what God desires from us as reborn children.

> There is a judge for the one who rejects me
> and does not accept my words; that very word
> which I spoke will condemn him at the last day.
> For I did not speak of my own accord, but the
> Father who sent me commanded me what to
> say and how to say it. —**John 12:48-49**

Jesus came to rescue us from the grip of sin and Satan and restore us to our rightful place as God's children. This means that Jesus did not just come to forgive us of our sins; He came to bring spiritual rebirth so that we could be restored as the children of God that we were created to be. The Son of God— Jesus—became human, so that humans could once again become sons of God.

Because of sin, we have lost our ability to live in our identities as children of God. But Jesus was sinless, so He was able to demonstrate to us *how to live* in our originally created design as children of God. (Refer back to the lesson from *Day 2*).

Jesus came to do what Adam—the first human—failed to do. Jesus lived perfectly in His created design as God's child.

> ...for he (Jesus) faced all of the same testings we
> do, yet he did not sin. —**Hebrews 4:15b NLT**

It is God's desire for us to become like Jesus.

> For those God foreknew he also predestined to
> be conformed to the image of his Son, that he
> might be the firstborn among many brothers
> and sisters. —**Romans 8:29**

This means that a Christian is not someone who simply believes in Jesus. A Christian is someone who lives like Jesus, through the power of Jesus. Christians become like Christ. (We will learn more about this on *Day 14.)*

> So all of us who have had that veil removed can see and reflect the glory of the Lord. *And the Lord—who is the Spirit—makes us more and more like him as we are changed into his glorious image.*
> —**2 Corinthians 3:18 NLT** *(Emphasis added)*

This is where the word *Christian* is derived from. The suffix, *-ian,* means *adhering to, following or resembling.* A Christian adheres to, follows and resembles Christ. They have placed Him in charge of their lives and they live like Jesus lived.

> You must have the same attitude that Christ Jesus had. —**Philippians 2:5**

> Whoever claims to live in him must live as Jesus did. —**1 John 2:6**

1. **Had you ever considered that Jesus did not only come to die on behalf of you and your sins, but also came to teach you how to live? What are your thoughts concerning this?**

OBEDIENCE TO JESUS

Jesus insisted that His words came from God.

> He who does not love me will not obey my teaching. These words you hear are not my own; they belong to the Father who sent me.
> —**John 14:24**

Jesus fully expected His followers to obey His teachings.

> "Why do you call me, 'Lord, Lord,' and do not
> do what I say?" —**Luke 6:46**

Furthermore, God Himself validated who Jesus is and told the
disciples to listen to Him.

> While he was still speaking, a bright cloud
> covered them, and a voice from the cloud said,
> "This is my Son, whom I love; with him I am
> well pleased. *Listen to him!"* —**Matthew 17:15**
> *(Emphasis added)*

Jesus stated that obedience to His teachings saves us from destruction.

> "Therefore everyone who hears these words of
> mine and *puts them into practice* is like a wise
> man who built his house on the rock. The rain
> came down, the streams rose, and the winds
> blew and beat against that house; yet it did
> not fall, because it had its foundation on the
> rock. But everyone who hears these words of
> mine and *does not put them into practice* is like
> a foolish man who built his house on sand.
> The rain came down, the streams rose, and the
> winds blew and beat against that house, and
> it fell with a great crash." — Matthew 7:24-27
> *(Emphasis added)*

Jesus commissioned His followers to go make new disciples, and
to teach His new disciples to obey everything He commanded. A
disciple literally means *one who is trained*. Therefore, a disciple of
Jesus is someone who is trained in His ways. They learn to see
and live life from Jesus' point of view.

> Then Jesus came to them and said, "All
> authority in heaven and on earth has been
> given to me. *Therefore go and make disciples of*

all nations, baptizing them in the name of the
Father and of the Son and of the Holy Spirit,
*and teaching them to obey everything I have
commanded you.* And surely I am with you
always, to the very end of the age."
—**Matthew 28:18-20** *(Emphasis added)*

**Other Scripture writers taught that obedience to Jesus
demonstrates that you know and trust Him.**

We know that we have come to know him if we
keep his commands. Whoever says, "I know
him," but does not do what he commands
is a liar, and the truth is not in that person.
Whoever claims to live in him must live as
Jesus did. —**1 John 2:3-6**

These are strong words that echo what Jesus   taught.

"Not everyone who says to me, 'Lord, Lord,'
will enter the kingdom of heaven, but only the
one who does the will of my Father who is in
heaven." —**Matthew 7:21**

Jesus taught us the will of the Father. Obedience to what Jesus
taught demonstrates that He is our Lord.

2. **Reread the previous Scriptures about obedience in this
    section. Which one(s) stand out to you? Why?**

the importance of Jesus' death

There is no denying that the central event in the life of Jesus was His death. It is also important to your life and identity.[11]

Jesus' death paid the full penalty of your sin. The Bible teaches that humanity owes God a huge debt. We have dishonored God. We have betrayed Him. We have earned death and Hell, which is the penalty reserved for Satan—God's enemy. None of us can escape this reality because we have all sinned, and as a result we are all spiritually dead.

> As for you, you were dead in your transgressions and sins... **—Ephesians 2:1**

> For the wages of sin is death, but the gift of God is eternal life in Christ Jesus our Lord. **—Romans 6:23**

> As it is written: "There is no one righteous, not even one…" **—Romans 3:10**

By becoming human and living sinlessly, Jesus was able to do for us what we could not do for ourselves. He made restitution to God on behalf of all humanity. He stood in our place.

> When Adam sinned, sin entered the world. Adam's sin brought death, so death spread to everyone, for everyone sinned. Yes, Adam's one sin brings condemnation for everyone, but Christ's one act of righteousness brings a right relationship with God and new life for everyone. Because one person disobeyed God, many became sinners. But because one other person obeyed God, many will be made righteous. **—Romans 5:12, 18-19 NLT**

> God made him who had no sin to be sin
> for us, so that in him we might become the
> righteousness of God. —**2 Corinthians 5:21**

Jesus stood in *your* place.

So when you trust Jesus with your life, you can say with full confidence, *"Jesus' death paid the full penalty of my sin."*

> We are made right with God by placing our
> faith in Jesus Christ. And this is true for
> everyone who believes, no matter who we are.
> For everyone has sinned; we all fall short of
> God's glorious standard. Yet God freely and
> graciously declares that we are righteous. He
> did this through Christ Jesus when he freed
> us from the penalty for our sins. For God
> presented Jesus as the sacrifice for sin. People
> are made right with God when they believe that
> Jesus sacrificed his life, shedding his blood...
> —**Romans 3:22-25b NLT**

1. **Why do you think a sinless person needed to stand in our place?**

Jesus' death is the ultimate example of sacrificial love. Jesus taught that laying down your life for your friends is the greatest example of love.

> Greater love has no one than this: to lay down one's life for one's friends. —**John 15:13**

Now notice this: Jesus did not only come to die for His friends. Jesus came to die for all of humanity who had become God's enemies.

> Very rarely will anyone die for a righteous person, though for a good person someone might possibly dare to die. But God demonstrates his own love for us in this: While we were still sinners, Christ died for us.
> —**Romans 5:7-8**

Jesus' death proved that you can trust God. Jesus did not just die any death. He felt the fullest extent of the evil in our world. Jesus restricted all of His limitless power as God, and allowed people to do to His body some of the worst things that people can do to each other.

Through His death, Jesus showed us the extremes to which He was freely willing to go to demonstrate His love and earn our trust. His love in action uncovered Satan's lie that we cannot trust God. It is as if Jesus said, "What more can I do to prove that you can trust me?"

> First, Christ said, "You did not want animal sacrifices or sin offerings or burnt offerings or other offerings for sin, nor were you pleased with them"(though they are required by the law of Moses). Then he said, "Look, I have come to do your will." He cancels the first covenant in order to put the second into effect. For God's will was for us to be made holy by the sacrifice of the body of Jesus Christ, once for all time.
> —**Hebrews 10:8-10 NLT**

2. Do you think that Jesus' death shows that we can trust God? Why or why not?

WHY DID JESUS HAVE TO DIE?

Many people wonder why God did not just forgive people, why did Jesus have to die? To forgive means to *erase a debt.* But when you think of it, a debt is never really erased. When someone forgives you of a debt that you owe them, *they* are absorbing what you owed them. For example, if you owed me $1,000 and I forgave you, I "ate the cost." In effect, I paid the debt for you.

In the same way, our penalty is eternal death. Through His own death, Jesus literally absorbed into His body the death penalty of our sin.[12]

Furthermore, the graphic, horrific nature of His death by crucifixion is a visual example of the terrible effect that sin has on humanity. It will forever serve as a reminder that *"the wages of sin is death, but the gift of God is eternal life in Christ Jesus our Lord!"* (Romans 6:23)

3. What does it mean to say that God "absorbed" the debt that we owed him?

the importance of Jesus' resurrection

Jesus did not just die. He *defeated* death and rose from the dead. There are several implications His resurrection has for us.

Jesus' resurrection proved that He is who He says He is. By defeating death, Jesus proved that He is indeed Lord of *all* things— including death—and therefore can be trusted to be Who He says He is. (See *Appendix II* for more information about the validity of Jesus' Resurrection)

> But God raised him from the dead, freeing him from the agony of death, because it was impossible for death to keep its hold on him. "Therefore let all Israel be assured of this: God has made this Jesus, whom you crucified, both Lord and Messiah." —**Acts 2:24,36**

1. **Do you think that defeating death by not staying dead proves that Jesus is Who He claimed to be—the Word of God in flesh—sent to redeem humanity? Why or why not?**

Jesus' Resurrection gave Him power over death and Hell.
Jesus did not just die to rescue us from the *penalty* of our sins. He defeated death and Hell giving Him *power* over them. He has the power to free *you* from their power.

> I [Jesus] am the Living One; I was dead, and
> now look, I am alive for ever and ever! And I
> hold the keys of death and Hades.
> —**Revelation 1:18**

Jesus frees you from sin and Satan's grip and returns you to God. He paid your ransom and brought you home to God. Scripture describes those living in the world as caught in a war between light and darkness. You were born into darkness. When you surrender to Jesus, He brings you out of the Kingdom of Darkness and into the Kingdom of Light.

> For Christ also suffered once for sins, the
> righteous for the unrighteous, to bring you to
> God. He was put to death in the body but made
> alive in the Spirit. —**1 Peter 3:18**

> ...and giving joyful thanks to the Father, who
> has qualified you to share in the inheritance of
> his holy people in the kingdom of light. For he
> has rescued us from the dominion of darkness
> and brought us into the kingdom of the Son
> he loves, in whom we have redemption, the
> forgiveness of sins. —**Colossians 1:12-14**

Jesus' Resurrection gives you the power to live a new life.
Christians are people who believe in Jesus. As a result, they live like Jesus through the Power of Jesus. Many people believe that they are not good enough to follow Jesus. They are afraid that they will fail and disappoint Him. But realize this: you will never be good enough. We all fail with our own efforts. This is why we need Jesus. He gives us power to live new lives.

For we died and were buried with Christ by baptism. And just as Christ was raised from the dead by the glorious power of the Father, now we also may live new lives. —**Romans 6:4**

2. **What do you think it means to say that Jesus gives us the power to live a new life?**

is Jesus Lord?

Jesus asked the following:

"Who do the crowds say I am?"

They replied, "Some say John the Baptist; others say Elijah; and still others, that one of the prophets of long ago has come back to life."

"But what about you?" he asked. "Who do you say I am?"

Peter answered, "God's Messiah."

—**Luke 9:18b-20**

After Jesus had died, was resurrected and returned to Heaven, Peter repeated this truth when he preached about Jesus.

"Therefore let all Israel be assured of this: God has made this Jesus, whom you crucified, both Lord and Messiah." —**Acts 2:36**

By claiming that Jesus is the Messiah, Peter used a Hebrew word that was familiar to the Jewish people. It denotes *The One anointed by God to save His people*.[13] The Jewish people of Jesus' day were waiting and looking for a person who was blessed and sent by God to save them from their Roman oppressors.

Through Jesus' teachings, death and resurrection, Peter understood the bigger implication of Jesus' mission. He recognized Jesus' divine ability to save the world from its real oppressors—Satan and sin. Peter recognized who Jesus is. Jesus is Lord.

1. What did Peter mean when he said Jesus was God's Messiah?

2. What does it mean to say that Jesus is Lord?

JESUS' CLAIM

Jesus did not claim to be just a prophet or a good teacher. He insisted that He is the *only* way to God.

> Jesus answered, "I am the way and the truth and the life. No one comes to the Father except through me." —**John 14:6**

This was an arrogant claim for Jesus to make—unless it is true.

If it is true, and Jesus is who He said He is —the Word of God in human flesh—then He is the only one in history who is in the unique position to save us and restore us to God. This claim is what separates Him from all other prophets or "holy men" of other religions. He is Lord. He is God in person.

Some ask, *How can I trust that Jesus is Lord? What gives Him the right to be in control of my life?* Let's look back at some key teachings about Jesus we have learned:

- Jesus has eternally existed as the Word of God. He has always been with God, and He is God. *(John 1:1)*

- All things were made for Jesus and by Jesus. *(Colossians 1:16; Romans 11:36)*

- Jesus was the part of God that became human flesh. He is God. *(Colossians 1:15; John 1:14)*

- While Jesus was on earth, God audibly spoke to the disciples and announced Who Jesus is and said that Jesus should be listened to. God confirmed that Jesus is Lord. *(Matthew 17:5)*

- Jesus Himself claimed to be God and claimed to speak for God. *(John 10:30; John 12:48-49)*

- Jesus claimed to be the only way to God. This is true because He *is* God. It is illogical to think that you can get to God, apart from God. *(John 14:26)*

- Finally, Jesus' resurrection proved that He is Who He said He is. Anyone can claim anything. But Jesus actually defeated death and proved that He is Lord—Supreme—over everything. *(Acts 2:24.36)*

Jesus' claim calls for a decision about who He is to you. Jesus still asks the question of humanity—He asks the question of you: "Who do you say that I am?"

C. S. Lewis, a popular Christian writer, put it this way:

> "A man who was merely a man and said the sort of things Jesus said would not be a great moral teacher. He would either be a lunatic—on the level with a man who says he is a poached egg—or He would be the devil of hell. You must make your choice. Either this was, and is, the Son of God, or else a madman or something worse. You can shut Him up for a fool or you can fall at His feet and call Him Lord and God. But let us not come with any patronizing nonsense about His being a great human teacher. He has not left that open to us."[14]

So Jesus is either *Lord*, a *liar*, or a delusional *lunatic*.

3. **Do you agree with C.S. Lewis' position here? Why or why not?**

If you believe that Jesus is Lord, then you know you can trust Him with your life. You know that rescue from a life ruined by sin comes from Him, and you know that your future is secure with Him.

Who do *you* say that He is? Is He God's Messiah and *Lord*? Can He save you from your sins and sinful nature and return you to your rightful place as a child of God? Or is He a *liar*? A *lunatic*?

notes

salvation–reborn identity

> "Jesus replied,
>
> "Very truly I tell you, no one can see the kingdom of God unless they are born again."
>
> —JOHN 3:3

grace & faith

How can you be saved from spiritual death and restored to your intended place as God's child?

> For it is by grace you have been saved, through faith— and this is not from yourselves, it is the gift of God... —**Ephesians 2:8**

The great Christian preacher John Wesley explained it this way, "Grace is the source, faith the condition, of salvation."[15]

GRACE—THE SOURCE OF SALVATION

It is impossible to save yourself. The result of sin is spiritual death. Because you are spiritually dead, no amount of effort on your part can bring you back to life. A dead person cannot rescue himself. Help must come from outside.

> As for you, you were dead in your transgressions and sins... —**Ephesians 2:1**

Salvation from sin and spiritual rebirth comes only through God's grace. Grace is God's kindness—His favor. In other words, you can only be saved because God, motivated by His love and kindness, took the initiative to extend to you the offer of salvation and spiritual rebirth.

> But because of his great love for us, God, who is rich in mercy, made us alive with Christ even when we were dead in transgressions— it is by grace you have been saved. —**Ephesians 2:4-5**

Nothing you do can earn the right to be saved. Many people sense their need for God and try to "get on His good side" by doing good deeds or by being a good person. It is as if they are attempting to show God that they are good enough to be saved.

Our best efforts are like dirty rags compared to God's righteousness and purity. Because He is holy, our good efforts can never impress Him. God saves us because He loves us, not because we have impressed Him.

> We are all infected and impure with sin. When we display our righteous deeds, they are nothing but filthy rags. Like autumn leaves, we wither and fall, and our sins sweep us away like the wind. —**Isaiah 64:6 NLT**

God has extended the offer of salvation to everyone. God has made it possible for all people—absolutely everyone—to be saved from death and to be spiritually reborn. He desires that no one would perish. He is patiently waiting for us to come home.

> The Lord is not slow in keeping his promise, as some understand slowness. Instead he is patient with you, not wanting anyone to perish, but everyone to come to repentance.
> —**2 Peter 3:9**

1. **Why can salvation only come from God and not from our own efforts?**

FAITH—THE CONDITION OF OUR SALVATION

Salvation requires a faith-filled response from you. The gift of salvation from God requires more than His patient desire for us to come home. You must respond to Him through faith—trust in Jesus—and *accept* God's offer of salvation and spiritual rebirth.

> If you declare with your mouth, "Jesus is Lord,"
> and believe in your heart that God raised him
> from the dead, you will be saved.
> —**Romans 10:9**

Your faith-filled response is only possible because of God's grace toward you. To say that you must respond through faith and accept God's offer does not mean that your faith-filled response is a work you need to produce to earn your salvation. Remember—without Christ, we are all spiritually dead. No effort on our part can change this.

> For it is by grace you have been saved, through
> faith— and this is not from yourselves, it is
> the gift of God— *not by works, so that no one can
> boast.* —**Ephesians 2:8-9** *(Emphasis added)*

Responding through faith means that God has given all people a "measure" of faith (Romans 12:3). This portion gives us the *ability* to believe that God exists, and gives us the *capacity* to respond to Him. This means that even the ability to respond to God's offer is placed into us by God. It is not something we produce in ourselves.

Our faith-filled response is simply *using* the faith that God has already placed in our hearts and choosing to trust in Jesus' Lordship.

Why is a response from us necessary for salvation? Many wonder why God does not just save everyone. Why must a person respond with faith in order to be saved?

Understand that a love-based relationship with humanity was

God's desire for creating us from the beginning. A love-based relationship is only possible when it involves the *choice* to stay or walk away.

If God automatically saved everyone, He would rob us of the choice to love Him or walk away from Him. Think about it—if you were forced to love Him, would it really be love?

God wants you to choose to love Him. Through Jesus, He has done everything necessary to make salvation possible for you, including providing the *ability* to choose Him! However, He will not force you to love and choose Him. You must decide that for yourself. He will not make that decision for you.

2. **Why does salvation require a decision from you? Why isn't it automatic?**

incomplete belief

> For God so loved the world that he gave his
> one and only Son, that whoever believes in him
> shall not perish but have eternal life.
> —**John 3:16**

What does it mean to truly believe in Jesus? Is mentally or verbally agreeing that Jesus is the Son of God enough to save you from your sins? Or is there more involved?

Many people base their salvation on the following actions or beliefs. According to Scripture, each of these is incomplete and can lead to a false assurance of salvation:[16]

Believing in God does not mean that you are saved. Even demons believe in God.

> You believe that there is one God. Good!
> Even the demons believe that—and shudder.
> —**James 2:19**

Believing that Jesus is the Son of God does not mean that you are saved. Even demons believe this—and they also believe that Jesus is the way to salvation.

> When he (a demon-possessed man) saw Jesus,
> he cried out and fell at his feet, shouting at the
> top of his voice, "What do you want with me,
> Jesus, Son of the Most High God? I beg you,
> don't torture me!" For Jesus had commanded
> the impure spirit to come out of the man.
> —**Luke 8:28-29a**

> She (a demon-possessed girl) followed Paul
> and the rest of us, shouting, "These men are
> servants of the Most High God, who are telling
> you the way to be saved." —**Acts 16:17**

Sensing the Presence of God does not mean that you are saved. Many people can sense God's Presence while in spiritual environments or in prayer. This does not mean that you are saved. The Old Testament recounts how God's Spirit came upon a murderer—King Saul—to delay his murderous plot. Although he experienced the Presence of God through this encounter, he was not saved. Afterward, he continued his murderous plans.

> So Saul went to Naioth at Ramah. But the Spirit
> of God came even on him, and he walked along
> prophesying until he came to Naioth.
> —**1 Samuel 19:23**

Performing supernatural acts or miracles does not mean that you are saved. Jesus warned that many supernatural acts and miracles will be performed by people who are not His.

> Not everyone who says to me, "Lord, Lord,"
> will enter the kingdom of heaven, but only the
> one who does the will of my Father who is in
> heaven. Many will say to me on that day, "Lord,
> Lord, did we not prophesy in your name and in
> your name drive out demons and in your name
> perform many miracles?" Then I will tell them
> plainly, "I never knew you. Away from me, you
> evildoers!" —**Matthew 7:21-23**

Doing good does not mean that you are saved. A saved life will result in good deeds, but good deeds alone will not save anyone. Many people look at the good things they have done and assume that if their good outweighs their bad they will be all right with God. This is a fatal assumption.

The question is not, *Have I done enough good deeds?* The question is, *Have I ever done bad deeds—have I ever sinned?* If you have done any bad deeds—even only one—then you are spiritually dead and no amount of good deeds can restore spiritual life. Only spiritual rebirth through Jesus can do that.

> For the wages of sin is death, but the gift of
> God is eternal life in Christ Jesus our Lord.
> —**Romans 6:23**

Feeling sorry for your sins does not mean that you are saved. People can be sorry for their sins for many different reasons: sorry they were caught, made to feel guilty, fear of punishment, etc. But Scripture states that only true sorrow—Godly sorrow— leads to repentance—change—which leads to salvation.

> For the kind of sorrow God wants us to
> experience leads us away from sin and results
> in salvation. There's no regret for that kind
> of sorrow. But worldly sorrow, which lacks
> repentance, results in spiritual death.
> —**2 Corinthians 7:10 NLT**

Reciting a prayer and being baptized does not mean that you are saved. Jesus said that many will *say* He is their Lord but will not enter Heaven. (Reference Matthew 7:21-24 again). After all, anyone can say anything.

All of these things are *important*, but doing or experiencing one or all of them does not mean that you are saved. These things are at best a verbal acknowledgment or a mental agreement with spiritual concepts—that is not enough to save you from the effects and penalty of sin in your life and your ensuing spiritual death.

You must believe *in your heart* in order to be saved. (*Romans 10:9-10*)

1. Does it surprise or concern you that any of these things are false assurances of salvation? If so, which ones and why?

faith that saves

If you declare with your mouth, "Jesus is Lord," and believe in your heart that God raised him from the dead, you will be saved. For it is with your heart that you believe and are justified, and it is with your mouth that you profess your faith and are saved. As Scripture says, "Anyone who believes in him will never be put to shame." —**Romans 10:9-11**

WHAT DOES IT MEAN TO BELIEVE IN YOUR HEART?

Because your heart is the center of your emotions and desires, to believe in your heart and to call Jesus Lord means that you have fully surrendered your desires and will to His Lordship. You trust Him with your life

You do not just *say* that you trust Him; you demonstrate your trust in Jesus by actually relying upon Him.

Think of it like this: You can agree that a ladder is sturdy, even sturdy enough to support your weight, but that does not mean that you trust it. Your belief that the ladder will support you is only shown when you actually stand upon it. When you stand upon it, you rely on it to support you. *Your words and actions agree* that the ladder can be trusted.[17]

Scripture teaches us that faith (belief) without action (acting on that belief) is dead (useless).

> In the same way, faith by itself, if it is not accompanied by action, is dead. But someone will say, "You have faith; I have deeds." Show me your faith without deeds, and I will show you my faith by my deeds. You believe that there is one God. Good! Even the demons believe that—and shudder. —**James 2:17-19**

Again, this passage teaches that if your faith does not result in action, then it is no better than that of a demon.

So true belief—heart belief—results in the faith-filled response of surrendering the control of your life to Jesus and trusting in Him. Remember, even the ability to believe is a gift from God, so nothing that you produce by your efforts can earn your salvation. Salvation comes through the faith-filled response of fully relying on Who Jesus is and what He has done.

Therefore, when you *truly believe* in your heart that Jesus is Lord over all things including death, you will rely fully on Him to take care of every aspect of your life.

- You trust Jesus with your past. You understand that your good efforts can never reverse your sinful nature and spiritual death. As a result, you believe and fully trust that Jesus' sacrifice can.

- You trust Jesus with your present. Because He is your Lord and is in control of your life, His Spirit and teachings guide your decisions and actions. You become His disciple—His student. You don't simply agree that He is right; you demonstrate your trust in Him by actually doing what He says.

- You trust Jesus with your future. Because you trust your life in His hands, you do not need to fear what the future holds, including death. You know that He has conquered the power of death, and can and will safely lead you through whatever death holds and will forever reunite you with God.

In other words, you "stand on the ladder" and trust that it will support all of you. Although self-sufficient people might acknowledge or agree with who Jesus is, this is one thing that they—along with Satan and his demons—will never do. They will not trust Jesus enough to surrender their will and desires—the lordship (control) of their life—to Him.

1. What is the difference between mentally OR verbally agreeing that Jesus is Lord, and actually surrendering the control of your life to Him?

surrender & repentance

If you truly believe Jesus is who He said He is—God in flesh, Lord of all things, even death— you know that you can trust Him with your life. As a result, you release control of your life and surrender to Him. You turn from *your* way of doing things and follow Him.

SURRENDER

We either live in submission to God or in rebellion against Him. Mankind's rebellion against God is what separated us from Him in the beginning and brought us spiritual and physical death.

Because rebellion against God is the source of sin and separation from God, humility through surrender to Him is the only path back to restoration.

> But he gives us more grace. That is why
> Scripture says: "God opposes the proud but
> shows favor to the humble." —**James 4:6**

Surrender is giving control of your life to Christ. You stop resisting God; you begin trusting Him with your life. Surrender is full reliance upon Jesus. Because self-reliance leads us away from God, only complete reliance on Him can bring us back to Him.

> If you cling to your life, you will lose it; but if
> you give up your life for me, you will find it.
> —**Matthew 10:39 NLT**

When you surrender your life to the Lordship of Jesus and are spiritually reborn, you *start life over* and begin *relearning everything* with Jesus as your Teacher. Jesus said that we are to be born again and become like a child.

And he said: "Truly I tell you, unless you change and become like little children, you will never enter the kingdom of heaven."
—**Matthew 18:3**

Surrender to Jesus does not mean that you will be perfect. But it does mean that Jesus is in charge of your life; you have decided in advance that He is right. You intend to spend the rest of your life learning and following what He desires.

1. **What does it mean to decide in advance that Jesus is right?**

REPENTANCE

The identity of being a child of God is offered to everyone. You must turn from your way of doing things and surrender to the Lordship of Jesus. In other words, you must repent. The word "repent" means to *turn or change*.[18]

Repentance simply means that you change from your way of doing things and turn toward doing things God's way. You cannot live life your way and God's way at the same time. The roads go in opposite directions. You must turn from one in order to travel on the other.

If you refuse to repent—turn from your sinful desires and ways and toward God's will—you have not surrendered your heart to Jesus. You are still living in rebellion against God. Repentance—change—is the natural product of a surrendered heart.

How can you say that Jesus is in charge of your life yet ignore Him and do what you want? You can "con" a lot of people in life, but you can't "con" Jesus. He knows the truth. If He is your Lord, you will do what He says.

"Why do you call me, 'Lord, Lord,' and do not do what I say?" —**Luke 6:46**

As we have learned, surrender and repentance involves more than just saying that Jesus is Lord. It involves an actual change in behavior. Your created design as God's child becomes evident as you begin to do His will..

This is what Jesus meant when He stated,

> "Not everyone who says to me, 'Lord, Lord,' will enter the kingdom of heaven, but only the one who does the will of my Father who is in heaven." —**Matthew 7:21**

Let's be clear—doing the will of God does not save you. That would mean that your works or efforts can save you. However, when you surrender yourself, you *want* to do the will of the Father. You turn from your desires and yield to the Father's desires and will.

2. **What is the difference between doing the will of God because you are saved rather than doing the will of God to try to earn your salvation?**

Surrender to God's will does not mean that you will never desire to sin again. Old desires still exist, but when we are spiritually reborn, God places new desires in us. While we learn to follow Jesus, we learn how to overcome our old desires. Repentance and surrender is an ongoing process that *begins* with our initial decision to follow Jesus. We then learn how to daily "live out" that decision.

> So I say, walk by the Spirit, and you will not gratify the desires of the flesh. —**Galatians 5:16**

WHAT MOTIVATES TRUE REPENTANCE AND SURRENDER?

When you realize the magnitude of sin's destruction in your life and how hurtful and offensive it is to God, you will understand what a gift you have been given—by God's grace and His willingness to forgive you. You will see God for Who He is—a loving Father who desires His child to come home. You see yourself for who you are—a rebellious child who has betrayed and hurt your Father.

These realizations produce true sorrow. You are not sorry because you got caught or because you have hurt others or yourself. You are truly sorry because you know you have hurt your Father.

This type of Godly sorrow motivates repentance—change. Repentance brings salvation.

> Godly sorrow brings repentance that leads to salvation and leaves no regret, but worldly sorrow brings death. —**2 Corinthians 7:10**

When completely humbled by the extravagant love of God, the only logical response is to extravagantly love Him in return. You come to love Him more than sin, more than your desires, more than other attachments—more than anything.

"All of me for all of You," is the natural response to Jesus' love.

> See what great love the Father has lavished on us, that we should be called children of God! And that is what we are! —1 John 3:1a NLT

3. **Reflect on how truly precious the gift of God's offer to save you and bring you home is.**

have you been born again?

> Jesus replied, "Very truly I tell you, no one can see the kingdom of God unless they are born again." —**John 3:3**

What Jesus offers is not just forgiveness of sins, but rather He offers the chance to be spiritually reborn and returned to our place as God's child. Jesus taught us that we cannot enter the Kingdom of God—be returned to our Father as His child—unless we are born again.

This means that the question is not simply, *Have you been forgiven?* Scripture makes it clear that Jesus paid the penalty of sin.

> For God was in Christ, reconciling the world to himself, no longer counting people's sins against them. And he gave us this wonderful message of reconciliation.
> —**2 Corinthians 5:19 NLT**

The problem is this: your sin has already resulted in your spiritual death. You are *already* spiritually dead in your sins against God. Your spiritual death will result in eternal death—separation from God in Hell. But God has made a way for you to be made alive again.

> As for you, you were dead in your transgressions and sins...like the rest, we were by nature deserving of wrath. But because of his great love for us, God, who is rich in mercy, made us alive with Christ even when we were dead in transgressions—it is by grace you have been saved. —**Ephesians 2:1, 3b-5**

The thought assumed by many after their surrender to Christ is that we are still the same person that we were before, only now we are forgiven. That is not what Scripture teaches. Scripture makes it clear that through salvation and baptism, who you *were* is gone—buried. God has resurrected your spirit to *new life!* The old has gone, the new has come. You are *not* the same person as before—you have been born again.

> For we died and were buried with Christ by baptism. And just as Christ was raised from the dead by the glorious power of the Father, now we also may live new lives. —**Romans 6:4**

In other words, when you surrender to Jesus, He doesn't just forgive you and pardon your crimes. He changes you into something other than a criminal. You are a child of God.

Being born again is not a metaphor!

1. **What is the difference between being forgiven and being changed?**

THE TEST OF GENUINE FAITH

So the real question is: *Have I been spiritually reborn and returned to my created design as a child of God?*

Before you answer, "Yes," make sure that your faith is true faith— saving faith. Apostle Paul taught us to examine ourselves to make sure our faith is genuine. Is there evidence of a new creation inside of you? Is the fruit of a changed life present in you?

> Examine yourselves to see if your faith is genuine. Test yourselves. Surely you know that Jesus Christ is among you; if not, you have failed the test of genuine faith.
> —**2 Corinthians 13:5 NLT**

Being sincere with God in prayer, feeling sorry for your sins and asking for forgiveness are a good start, but not enough to save you. Remember, there are false assurances of salvation. Many people have been deceived into thinking that a mere mental agreement that there is a God or that Jesus is the Son of God is enough to save them. As previously taught, even demons believe this—but it is not enough; it won't lead to a new heart in Jesus. . (James 2:19-20)

In order to be saved, you must surrender to Jesus' Lordship. When you surrender to and acknowledge His Lordship, His Holy Spirit enters into you and brings a new nature—a new heart.

TEST YOURSELF

Ask yourself, *"Has my belief led me to fully trust and rely on Jesus?"* In other words, *"Have I surrendered the control of my life to Him? Is there evidence that He is Lord of my life?*

If Jesus is your Lord, then there will be evidence in your life of His Presence. There will be signs of spiritual rebirth. You don't have to wonder if a baby has been born. Its presence is proof of its birth.

> Whoever says, "I know him," but does not do
> what he commands is a liar, and the truth is not
> in that person. But if anyone obeys his word,
> love for God is truly made complete in them.
> This is how we know we are in him: Whoever
> claims to live in him must live as Jesus did.
> —1 John 2:4-6

Among other things, a spiritually reborn child of God will:

- Have the desires of Jesus

- Demonstrate the actions of Jesus

- Live through the Power of Jesus

This is the fruit of a surrendered heart and a born again spirit.

We will learn more about these truths as we progress in our study but now it is important to do a "gut check" and answer in the way that only you can: *Is there evidence of a new person in me?*

> Therefore, if anyone is in Christ, the new creation has come: the old has gone, the new is here! —**2 Corinthians 5:17**

Having a new nature does *not* mean that you cannot or will not ever sin again. You will still have old, sinful habits and desires that you need to overcome. (We will learn more about this in *Workbook 2: Freedom*.)

Having the Nature of Christ *does* mean that you will have new desires. You will *desire* to turn from sin toward God. You will learn to cooperate with the Holy Spirit and allow those new desires to grow in you.

> So I say, walk by the Spirit, and you will not gratify the desires of the flesh. —**Galatians 5:16**

Perhaps you think that questions like these are judgmental and that Jesus taught us not to judge.

It is true that Jesus taught us in Matthew 7:1-4 that we should not judge or condemn others —specifically, that we should not act like others' sins are worse than our own. However, in that same passage Jesus clearly taught that we should not believe the words of everyone who calls Him, "Lord." Rather, we should examine the fruit their lives produce.

> "Beware of false prophets who come disguised as harmless sheep but are really vicious wolves. You can identify them by their fruit, that is, by the way they act...
>
> Yes, just as you can identify a tree by its fruit, so you can identify people by their actions."
> —**Matthew 7:15-16, 20 NLT**

Jesus taught us that we should not take people at face value. He said that there are wolves who masquerade in sheep's clothing. On the surface they look and act a certain way, but on further inspection, it is clear that they are something else. The fruit of their actions reveals the condition of their hearts.

This lesson is not intended to make you question the validity of others and who they claim to be, but to rather look at your own life and test your own faith.

Is there evidence of a new creation—new desires inside you? If the new is not present, then it is time to re-examine your motives and fully surrender to the Lordship of Jesus. Allow His Spirit to fill you, remove your old nature and replace it with a new life.

> I will give you a new heart and put a new spirit in you; I will remove from you your heart of stone and give you a heart of flesh. And I will put my Spirit in you and move you to follow my decrees and be careful to keep my laws.
> —Ezekiel 36:26-27

If you confess to be a Christian, answer the following question. If you do not, then continue on to the next lesson.

2. **Is there evidence of a new person—new desires inside of you— after your salvation? If so, describe it.**

If not, then review *Day 19: Surrender and Repentance,* and reconsider if you truly surrendered the Lordship of your life to Jesus.

what happens when you surrender to Jesus?

In order to be born again, you must turn from your own way of living and surrender to the Lordship of Jesus. When you surrender, this is what happens:

You are forgiven and saved from the penalty of your sins.

> For everyone has sinned; we all fall short of God's glorious standard. Yet God freely and graciously declares that we are righteous. He did this through Christ Jesus when he freed us from the penalty for our sins. For God presented Jesus as the sacrifice for sin. People are made right with God when they believe that Jesus sacrificed his life, shedding his blood...
> —**Romans 3:23-25a NLT**

The Holy Spirit enters into you; you are spiritually reborn as a child of God. You are made alive. Your spirit is no longer dead!

> Humans can reproduce only human life, but the Holy Spirit gives birth to spiritual life.
> —**John 3:6 NLT**

> But to all who believed him and accepted him, he gave the right to become children of God. They are reborn—not with a physical birth resulting from human passion or plan, but *a birth that comes from God.* —**John 1:12-13 NLT** *(Emphasis added)*

The Holy Spirit will give you a new heart—a new nature. When you are spiritually reborn, you receive the Nature of Christ. In other words, you are not only pardoned for your crimes, you are now no longer a criminal. You have become a child of God.

> And because of his glory and excellence, he has given us great and precious promises. These are the promises that *enable you to share his divine nature and escape the world's corruption caused by human desires.* —**2 Peter 1:4 NLT** *(Emphasis added)*

> And I will give you a new heart, and I will put a new spirit in you. I will take out your stony, stubborn heart and give you a tender, responsive heart. —**Ezekiel 36:26 NLT**

Remember, having a new nature does *not* mean that you will never desire to sin again. Having the Nature of Christ *does* mean that you will have *new desires.* You will desire to turn from sin toward God and become the child of God you were created to be.

The Holy Spirit will then give you the assurance that you are a child of God. As his spiritually reborn child, you no longer need to fear death and Hell.

> The Spirit you received does not make you slaves, so that you live in fear again; rather, the Spirit you received brought about your adoption to sonship. And by him we cry, "Abba, Father." The Spirit himself testifies with our spirit that we are God's children. —**Romans 8:15-16**

The question remains, "Who do *you* say Jesus is?" Do you truly believe He is Lord and can be trusted with your life? Have you surrendered to His Lordship? Will you accept His offer of salvation?

SPIRITUAL ASSESSMENT

Take a moment to determine your current reaction to Jesus' message:

☐ I do not believe that God exists and I have no desire to know more about Him.

☐ I desire to know if God even exists.

☐ I believe that God exists, but I am unsure if Jesus is the way to God.

☐ I believe that Jesus is the Way to God, but I have not surrendered to His Lordship.

☐ I have surrendered to Jesus' Lordship.

how to be born again

If you have not yet surrendered to Jesus' Lordship but are ready, here is what to do:

Admit that you have failed God, are spiritually dead and are in need of His help. At this point you may not even realize all of the ways you have failed God. However, you do realize that you have failed Him and cannot save yourself. You no longer make excuses or deny it. You admit it and want Him to save you from your sin and restore you back to your place as His child.

> Everyone who calls on the name of the Lord
> will be saved. —**Romans 10:13**

Believe that Jesus is Who He says He is. You believe that Jesus is Who He says He is—God in the flesh sent to save humanity—and you fully trust Him with your life. Your past, present and future are placed into His hands.

> If you declare with your mouth, "Jesus is Lord,"
> and believe in your heart that God raised him
> from the dead, you will be saved.
> —**Romans 10:9**

Confess Jesus as your Lord. To confess means to agree. If you have done the other two things, it is now time to agree that Jesus is Lord by saying it and believing it:

"Jesus I surrender to you. I acknowledge that I am unable to escape sin and death on my own. Please save me from sin and death. Please give me your Holy Spirit and bring me back to life again! You are Lord of my life. Through your power, I leave my old life of sin. I will live life following your will."

If you are ready to surrender to Jesus' Lordship, talk to God about those statements you just made. It is not necessary to wait for someone else to pray with you. If you are ready to surrender to Jesus and accept your identity as a child of God, do it *now*.

For he says, "In the time of my favor I heard you, and in the day of salvation I helped you." I tell you, now is the time of God's favor, now is the day of salvation. —**2 Corinthians 6:2**

1. **Consider writing out your prayer of repentance and surrender here:**

Congratulations on beginning your new life in Christ. There is celebration in Heaven because you came home!

In the same way, I tell you, there is rejoicing in the presence of the angels of God over one sinner who repents." —**Luke 15:10**

2. Review *Appendix III: God's Promises for His Children.* At your next group meeting, be prepared to talk about which of these stand out to you and why.

BAPTISM

If you have surrendered your life to Jesus, you should be baptized in water by another follower of Jesus. To baptize means "to immerse." This act reenacts Christ's burial and resurrection. We go under the water, and are raised out of the water—new.

Baptism was commanded by Jesus and incorporated into regular church practice by His Apostles.

> Therefore go and make disciples of all nations, baptizing them in the name of the Father and of the Son and of the Holy Spirit, and teaching them to obey everything I have commanded you. And surely I am with you always, to the very end of the age. —**Matthew 28:19-20**

> Peter replied, "Repent and be baptized, every one of you, in the name of Jesus Christ for the forgiveness of your sins. And you will receive the gift of the Holy Spirit. —**Acts 2:38**

Baptism is a public announcement of your decision to bury your past and live a new life with Jesus as your Lord.

> We were therefore buried with him through baptism into death in order that, just as Christ was raised from the dead through the glory of the Father, we too may live a new life. —**Romans 6:4**

REBAPTISM

Some people consider re-baptism for the following reasons:

They were baptized as an infant or child and did not understand the decision made on their behalf.

They have renewed their decision to follow Christ and wish to signify that new commitment. (In the same way that many couples choose to renew wedding vows.)

3. **What is stopping you from being baptized?**

4. **Whom will you contact to be baptized?**

factors that block surrender

"If you declare with your mouth, "Jesus is Lord," and believe in your heart that God raised him from the dead, you will be saved."
—ROMANS 10:9

doubt

Modern and post-modern ways of thinking are common outlooks that make belief in God and the Bible difficult.

Modernists want proof; truth is defined by what they see, hear, smell, taste and touch.

A post-modernist accepts sincerity, and ultimately believes people make their own truth; religious beliefs can be true and right for someone, but not for them.

Jesus provides a different perspective:

> Jesus answered, "I am the way and the truth and the life. No one comes to the Father except through me. —**John 14:6**

Jesus' claim raises a lot of questions for many people.

It is not wrong to have questions.

Questions are normal; but they can produce doubt about God. Instead of stopping in doubt, look for answers. Do not be close-minded; identify your questions and seek their answers.

Turn to *Appendix II: Essential Christian Beliefs,* and explore questions and evidence of the validity of some essential beliefs of the Christian faith.

1. **Which doubts or questions about God keep you away from Him?**

WHAT IS FAITH ?

Faith is not the absence of doubt. Faith is necessary when you *do* have doubts.[19] When you cannot know something with 100 percent certainty, whom or what do *you* trust? Others? Yourself? God? Faith in God is the *decision* to trust God when you have doubts.

Faith in God is not always blind. Many people think that believing in God is choosing to believe blindly in something which has no proof for its existence. However, if you look, you will find much that indicates the presence of God in the Universe.

> For ever since the world was created, people
> have seen the earth and sky. Through
> everything God made, they can clearly see
> his invisible qualities—his eternal power and
> divine nature. So they have no excuse for not
> knowing God. —**Romans 1:20**

Faith in God is trusting that God exists and that He rewards those who seek to know Him.

> And without faith it is impossible to please
> God, because anyone who comes to him must
> believe that he exists and that he rewards those
> who earnestly seek him
> —**Hebrews 11:6**

2. **Does this idea differ from what you have thought about faith? If yes, in what ways?**

HOW TO FIND FAITH DESPITE YOUR DOUBTS

While you seek answers to your questions, seek God Himself.
Remember that God is not just an idea or a belief. He is a Person you can know and relate to. Rather than just focusing on doubts about God or certain religious beliefs, seek to know God Himself.

> You will seek me and find me when you seek me with all your heart. —**Jeremiah 29:13**

Allow Jesus to speak for Himself. The four Gospels are written accounts about Jesus' life and teachings. Read them and let Jesus speak for Himself. Begin with the Gospel of John—it contains a large amount of Jesus' teachings and claims.

3. **Do you think it would help you to understand Jesus better if you allowed Him to speak for Himself by reading one of the Gospels? Why or why not?**

If you need faith, ask God for it. He promises He will give it to you. He promises that as you take steps toward Him, He will take steps toward you. Choosing to be engaged in this study is a step toward God. Believe that He will reveal Himself to you.

> Immediately the boy's father exclaimed, "I do believe; help me overcome my unbelief!"
> —**Mark 9:24**

> Come near to God and he will come near to you. —**James 4:8a**

Pause right now and ask God to give you faith. Even if you have never prayed, consider asking God to help your unbelief. Believe that He will reward your pursuit to know Him.

control

Surrendering your life to Jesus means that you give up control. If you are in control, you do what you want. If Jesus is control, you do what honors Him.

In our pride and arrogance, like Adam and Eve, we tend to believe Satan's lie that *we* should be allowed to make the rules. We believe the lie that *we* should be in control of our lives.[20] The problem with this is that *we are not God.* God created us in His image and knows what is best for us.

Our human minds were not designed to handle being in control; yet the feeling of being in control of *something* is addictive. It is difficult to let go, even when things quickly get beyond what we can handle. As a result, stress, worry, anxiety, anger and depression set in.

In fact, most of our problems come from trying to be in control.

> ...In the pride of your heart you say, "I am a
> god... But you are a mere mortal and not a god,
> though you think you are as wise as a god."
> —**Ezekiel 28:2**

Control is an illusion. When you think about it, you will see that there are very few things truly within your control. You cannot control most circumstances or people. You can only manage what you do and how you react. Even that can be difficult.

1. **In what ways has making your own rules led you to make choices that hurt you or others?**

2. In what ways has trying to control circumstances and people in your life left you stressed, worried, anxious, angry and/or depressed?

3. Which areas of your life seem out of control right now?

4. How does it make you feel to realize that you can relax and allow God to take control and help you get through life?

fear

Adam and Eve listened to and believed a lie about God. The lie made them distrust Him and want to take over control of their own lives. That opened the door to sin and death and they walked through it, taking humanity with them.

The result of eating the forbidden fruit and swallowing the lie is that their understanding of God and His kind, loving nature became distorted. It also brought a new kind of awareness about themselves. They hid from God because they were ashamed of their sin and nakedness. They felt exposed and vulnerable.

Adam and Eve left truth and trust behind and found fear. This kind of fear is not the "fear" or respect for God that we should have out of honor for Who He is. The kind of fear their sin introduced was fear based on *distrust*.

As a result of Adam and Eve's rejection of God, you were born into a world full of sin, death and destruction. It is easy to misunderstand God and be afraid of Him.

To make matters worse, when people try to impose their religious views on others (often in the name of God and with mostly good intentions) fears are often compounded. As a result, we often have misconceptions about God.

It is true that God does not love your sin. However, the Bible is clear that God loves *you*. He loves you enough to come to you through Jesus, to forgive you and change you.

> This is how God showed his love among us: He sent his one and only Son into the world that we might live through him. —**1 John 4:9**

1. **In what ways have the actions of religious people made you afraid to turn to God?**

You might be afraid that church people will judge you. You may fear that you are not "good" enough. You might be anxious about what type of things you will need to change or give up in order to follow Jesus. You might even be frightened of the type of person God wants to "turn you into."

This is the wrong focus. Your first focus should be to simply love God—to return the love He has for you. When you love Him, you will desire to do what He wants.

Notice that this verse teaches that if you love God, you will not *be afraid* of Him:

> There is no fear in love. But perfect love drives out fear, because fear has to do with punishment. The one who fears is not made perfect in love. —1 John 4:18

2. **Have you ever considered that you should develop a relationship with God because you love Him and He loves you rather than because you fear Him?**

3. Why is it better to make changes because you love someone instead of out of fear?

4. In what ways is being driven by love easier than being driven by fear?

shame

Seeking personal fulfillment and meaning outside of God leads to sin and spiritual death. This is our situation before we accept and live in our created identify as children of God.

Although sin temporarily feels good it never truly satisfies. Have you ever felt ashamed—like Adam and Eve—after indulging in sin and choosing to disobey God? .

Like them, you likely find yourself wanting to hide from God. Guilt and shame may suddenly make you feel that God does not love you, has changed His mind about your value and no longer wants you.

However, the Bible teaches that God loves us despite our failures.

> But God demonstrates his own love for us in this: While we were still sinners, Christ died for us. —**Romans 5:8**

> "Come now, let us settle the matter," says the Lord. "Though your sins are like scarlet, they shall be as white as snow; though they are red as crimson, they shall be like wool."
> —**Isaiah 1:18**

God loves you despite your failures. There is nothing you have done or will do that He does not know. There is nothing He cannot or will not forgive. He knows you intimately and still loves you and desires for you to be with Him.

Jesus told a story about a young man who grew up and chose his own way. He left his father's house and eventually made choices that caused him to lose his identity as a beloved son. The son in his story represents us; the father represents God:

But while he was still a long way off, his father saw him and was filled with compassion for him; he ran to his son, threw his arms around him and kissed him.

The son said to him, "Father, I have sinned against heaven and against you. I am no longer worthy to be called your son."

But the father said to his servants, "Quick... Let's have a feast and celebrate. For this son of mine was dead and is alive again; he was lost and is found."

So they began to celebrate.

—**Luke 15:18-24**

1. **In what ways have your actions left you feeling ashamed?**

2. **In what ways have other people's actions brought shame on you?**

3. In what ways have you degraded yourself or allowed others to degrade you because you were ashamed?

4. How do you feel, knowing the truth that God loves you in spite of your sins?

YOUR RESPONSE TO THE MESSAGE OF THE GOSPEL

Let's take a moment to review what we have learned:

Creation: God originally created the world as it should be. His desire for creating humans was to have a family to share for eternity.

Separation: Mankind separated themselves from a relationship with God by pursuing their own desires (sin). Sin not only separates us from God, it brings spiritual death and destruction.

Redemption: God saw mankind's fallen state. He took on human flesh through Jesus, and did everything necessary to bring us back to Himself. Jesus taught us what God desires. His death paid our sin penalty. His resurrection and His Spirit give us the power to live new lives.

Decision: Jesus *will not* force you to choose Him and love Him. *You* must decide whom you will follow. Will you continue to live life your own way or will you surrender to Jesus' Lordship, be spiritually reborn and live a life reunited with God as His child? Will you love and choose God—Who created you, loves you and desires to rescue you?

SPIRITUAL ASSESSMENT

Once again, take a moment to determine your current response to Jesus' message:

☐ I do not believe that God exists and I have no desire to know more about Him.

☐ I desire to know if God even exists.

☐ I believe that God exists, but I am unsure if Jesus is the way to God.

☐ I believe that Jesus is the Way to God, but I have not surrendered to His Lordship.

☐ I have surrendered to Jesus' Lordship.

---

5. **Are you willing to work on moving into the next step? Why or why not?**

6. Do doubt, shame, control or fear keep you from following Jesus? If so, which one(s)?

7. What do you believe is your next step to address your roadblock(s)?

If you have not surrendered your life to Jesus and His Lordship, but are ready to, go back and review *Day 22: How to Be Born Again.*

The rest of this series is designed to help followers of Jesus grow in their relationship with Him. If you are not yet ready to submit to Jesus, you should work through what prevents you from doing so.

For help to work through questions you have about God, visit **discoverdiscipleship.com.**

living in your identity as a child of God

> "And now, just as you accepted Christ Jesus as your Lord, you must continue to follow him. Let your roots grow down into him, and let your lives be built on him.
>
> Then your faith will grow strong in the truth you were taught, and you will over flow with thankfulness."

—COLOSSIANS 2:6-7 NLT

your new identity

Congratulations on making the first Core Decision of your spiritual journey!

The Identity Decision:
I choose to accept and live in my identity as a child of God, by surrendering to the Lordship of Jesus.

Surrendering to Christ's Lordship and becoming a spiritually reborn child of God is the first step you will make on your spiritual journey. This is not the end—it is just the great beginning.

> And now, just as you accepted Christ Jesus as
> your Lord, you must continue to follow him.
> Let your roots grow down into him, and let
> your lives be built on him. Then your faith will
> grow strong in the truth you were taught, and
> you will overflow with thankfulness.
> —**Colossians 2:6-7 NLT**

LIVING IN YOUR REAL IDENTITY

Surrender to Jesus is not about gaining a feeling of religious superiority over others. Surrender is also not just a way to avoid a bad afterlife. Surrender to Jesus means that you have accepted Him and will live out your identity as a child of God.

You were created by God for God. You were created to love Him and bring Him honor. If you have surrendered your life to Jesus, you must now learn to live a life that reflects the new identity He has given you. Up to this point in your life, you have lived with false, substitute identities. But that is no longer who you are or how you live. You are a spiritually reborn child of God!

The True Source of security. As a child of God, you do not need to look to others or even to yourself to "fix" everything. You can relax and be secure in your role as His child. Your responsibilities as God's child are to listen to Him, trust Him and obey Him. If you do this, you can trust Him with the outcome.

1. Review Day 5. What things do you normally look to as a substitute rather than God to provide your Security?

The True Source of worth. As a child of God you were created to have a relationship with Him. If you have Him, you have unsurpassed worth. What others think of you longer defines you because you know that He loves you.

2. Review Day 6. What things do you normally look to as a substitute rather than God to provide your Worth?

The True Source of fulfillment. As a child of God, His love fills and fulfills you. You are free from the drive to pursue empty, Substitute Identities. You can "drink" from His love and purpose, and be satisfied.

3. Review Day 7. What things do you normally look to as a substitute rather than God to provide your Fulfillment?

BECOMING LIKE CHRIST

A Christian is someone who truly believes in Jesus — they believe He is Who He says He is, God in flesh, sent to redeem humanity — therefore, they live like Jesus through the Power of Jesus. As we previously learned, when you surrender to Jesus' Lordship, the Holy Spirit enters you and brings a new heart—the Nature of Jesus—into you. Jesus actually lives in and through you. The life you now live is not your own. You live as Christ lived.

Remember that a being a Christian means you are actually becoming *like Christ.* This is true because Christ is *living* though us.

> My old self has been crucified with Christ. It is
> no longer I who live, but Christ lives in me.
> —**Galatians 2:20a NLT**

4. Does the real definition of Christian differ from what usually comes to your mind when you hear the word "Christian?" If so, in what ways?

If you have a new nature and Jesus lives through you, then your characteristics will be the attitude and the mind of Christ. This is different from your natural nature.

> Your attitude should be the same as that of Christ Jesus... —**Philippians 2:5**

> As a prisoner for the Lord, then, I urge you to live a life worthy of the calling you have received. —**Ephesians 4:1**

CODE OF CONDUCT STATEMENT

I am a child of God. My father is the King of the Universe. When you look at me you see a Prince or Princess. My royal identity does not cause me to live with arrogance, but with dignity and responsibility. Because I am a child of God, I will reflect the values and honor of my Father.[21]

5. **Describe implications this statement has for you and your lifestyle.**

new creation, new desires

Exactly what are the new desires that God places in us through His Holy Spirit?

Because Jesus perfectly reflects the originally created design of a child of God, we look at His life, values and teachings as recorded in Scripture in to learn what He is like. When He is alive in us, these same desires will reflect in us.[22]

> My old self has been crucified with Christ. It is no longer I who live, but Christ lives in me.
> —**Galatians 2:20a NLT**

The desires and nature of Jesus are best reflected in the following two passages of Scripture; the first is often called *The Great Commandment:*

> Jesus replied: "'Love the Lord your God with all your heart and with all your soul and with all your mind.' This is the first and greatest commandment. And the second is like it: 'Love your neighbor as yourself.'"
> —**Matthew 22:37-39**

This passage teaches that love for God and love for people are God's greatest desires for His children. When we look back toward the beginning of Creation, we see that love for God and each other was part of God's intended design for His children. (Reference the lesson from *Day 2: Your Created Design)*

The second passage is often called *The Great Commission*. In it, Jesus stated that all authority has been given to Him. He then gave His followers a mission to go into all the world and make other disciples (followers) of Him. In essence, we are to bring God's rule to the world through Jesus Christ. This too is part of God's intended design for His children.

> Then Jesus came to them and said, "All authority in heaven and on earth has been given to me. Therefore go and make disciples of all nations, baptizing them in the name of the Father and of the Son and of the Holy Spirit, and teaching them to obey everything I have commanded you. And surely I am with you always, to the very end of the age."
> —**Matthew 28:18-20**

THE NEW DESIRES OF A REBORN CHILD OF GOD

A child of God desires to grow in their relationship with God, just as Jesus did. We just read *The Great Commandment*, where Jesus taught us that loving God is the most important thing in life. When we examine Jesus' life, we see the close relationship He has with the Father. He insisted that He did not do one thing that the Father did not instruct Him to do.

> Jesus gave them this answer: "I tell you the truth, the Son can do nothing by himself; he can only do what he sees his Father doing, because whatever the Father does, the Son also does."
> —**John 5:19**

Growing in your relationship with God will be demonstrated by a desire to be close to Him and to receive spiritual nourishment from His words found in the Bible.

For you did not receive a spirit that makes you a slave again to fear, but you received the Spirit of sonship. And by him we cry, "Abba, Father." The Spirit himself testifies with our spirit that we are God's children. —**Romans 8:15-16**

Like newborn babies, crave pure spiritual milk, so that by it you may grow up in your salvation. —**1 Peter 2:2**

A child of God desires to love and serve other people, just as Jesus did. In *The Great Commandment*, Jesus taught that loving our neighbor in the same way that we love ourselves is the second most important thing that God desires from us. When we examine His life and see how He loved and served others, even those who rejected Him — even His enemies — we see His nature. This is the nature that will be in you.

Your attitude should be the same as that of Christ Jesus: Who being in very nature God, did not consider equality with God something to be grasped, but made himself nothing, taking the very nature of a servant, being made in human likeness. —**Philippians 2:5-7**

A child of God desires to bear the image of God in the world and to complete the mission they are created to do, just as Jesus did. Jesus said that His mission is to seek and save the lost, destroy the works of the world, and reconcile the world back to God. His life, and ultimately His death and resurrection, are demonstration of this mission.

For the Son of Man came to seek and to save what was lost. —**Luke 19:10**

He who does what is sinful is of the devil, because the devil has been sinning from the beginning. The reason the Son of God appeared was to destroy the devil's work. —**1 John 3:8**

As we have read in *The Great Commission*, Jesus gave the command to continue His work in the world. The following two passages reaffirm this:

> For it is by grace you have been saved, through faith—and this is not from yourselves, it is the gift of God—not by works, so that no one can boast. For we are God's workmanship, *created in Christ Jesus to do good works, which God prepared in advance for us to do.* —**Ephesians 2:8-10** (*Emphasis added*)

> ...that God was reconciling the world to himself in Christ, not counting men's sins against them. And he has committed to us the message of reconciliation. —**2 Corinthians 5:19**

A child of God desires freedom from the power of sin. Because Jesus did not succumb to the power of sin, He did not need to become freed from it.

> For we do not have a high priest who is unable to sympathize with our weaknesses, but we have one who has been tempted in every way, just as we are —yet was without sin.
> —**Hebrews 4:15**

But because Jesus *did* overcome sin, when He lives in us we will desire to be free from sin in our lives. When you are spiritually reborn, you will begin to desire more of God and less of sin.

> For the sinful nature desires what is contrary to the Spirit, and the Spirit what is contrary to the sinful nature. They are in conflict with each other so that you do not do what you want.
> —**Galatians 5:17**

A child of God desires to honor God with all of His life and resources. Living in His created design as Son of God on earth is what Jesus always did. However, we have a long history with Substitute Identities which shape our values and vie for our resources. We must intentionally steer our lives away from the desires of the world and align our lives and resources around His priorities as children of God. This will not always be automatic and requires decisions and work.

> Do you not know that your body is a temple of the Holy Spirit, who is in you, whom you have received from God? You are not your own; you were bought at a price. Therefore honor God with your body. —**1 Corinthians 6:19-20**

This course is designed to help you identify and live out each of these Core Decisions in order to become like Jesus. (Learn more about this in *Day 30: Becoming a Disciple of Jesus*)

1. **Does it surprise you to learn that Christians will have the desires of Jesus growing in them? Why or why not?**

2. **Are any of these new desires surprising to you? Why or why not?**

the evidence
of Christ in you

The presence of new desires, a new attitude, and new characteristics are indications that Christ is in you and you are truly spiritually reborn.

Let's be clear—you cannot create these new desires in yourself by yourself. Your new nature is placed in you by the grace of God through your faith in Jesus. This desire is not about trying harder to be "good." It is allowing Christ's nature and His desires shape the type of person you become. These new desires might be weak at first, but if you have been born again, they are present and must be nurtured.

This does not mean that all of your old desires will be gone; however it does mean that Christ's desires will be present. If new desires are not present, it is a sign that Christ is not present in you. Scripture is clear that if we have the Spirit of Christ, we will live the way that Christ lived.

> Whoever says, "I know him," but does not do
> what he commands is a liar, and the truth is not
> in that person. But if anyone obeys his word,
> love for God is truly made complete in them.
> This is how we know we are in him: Whoever
> claims to live in him must live as Jesus did.
> —1 John 2:4-6

Many people—unbelievers as well as those who claim to be followers of Christ—try to exempt themselves from living as Christ did. They want to continue to live their lives doing what they want but still have the assurance of salvation.

How can anyone claim to have surrendered to Christ and not obey His teachings? They reject the Nature of Christ. In other words, they want to remain living like a criminal, but be assured that they will be pardoned for their crimes and not face punishment.

People like this want to continue to pursue their old, Substitute Identities in life—pursuing security, worth and fulfillment through themselves, people and things—yet still have the assurance of salvation when they die.

Scripture does not support this belief! Only surrender to the Lordship of Christ brings salvation. If you surrender to His Lordship, you will live as He lived. (Reread 1 John 2:4-6 above)

Many people read Christ's commands and teachings and believe that it is acceptable to simply say, *I do not feel "called" to do that. Or, I don't have time for that. Or, That's too difficult for me to do. Or, I know I'm not following Christ's commands, but I'm okay with God.*

These are dangerous assumptions. Remember that there are many false assurances of salvation. As we have read, Jesus stated, "Not everyone who says to me, 'Lord, Lord,' will enter the kingdom of heaven, but only the one who does the will of my Father who is in heaven." (Matthew 7:21)

Let's be clear again—simply doing the will of God does not save you. That would mean your works can save you. However if you are truly saved, Christ lives in you and does the will of God through you. How can we honestly think that Christ will live through us in a way that is different from how He lived while on earth?

The principles and teachings that you are learning in this course show you how Jesus lived His life. If these things are His priorities, why would He live any differently through you? If He truly lives in you, these desires are present. At first they may be weak, but they are present and will grow as you mature in Him.

1. List one or two new desires that have been present in your life after you surrendered to Jesus.

Having Christ's nature in you does not mean that doing the right thing will always be easy. Apostle Paul described doing the right thing as a battle or struggle inside of him.

> But there is another power within me that is
> at war with my mind. This power makes me a
> slave to the sin that is still within me.
> —**Romans 7:23**

This is actually a sign that Christ is in you. The struggle between your old and new desires will be present. Now you don't just automatically "let yourself of the hook" mentally and keep sinning. In other words, you know what the right thing is—even if you want to resist it. You do not make excuses. You state it for what it is. You may even think, "*I know Jesus is right. I know I should change, but it's hard.*" That is why you must rely on the power of the Holy Spirit to give you His power to live a new life. (We explore this in detail in *Book 2: Discover Freedom*)

If a struggle is not present within you, and you continue to pursue sin as a normal lifestyle and think nothing of it, then new desires are not in you because the Spirit of Christ is not in you.

If that is the case, and you do not want to live a life in disobedience to God, go back to *Day 20: Have You Been Born Again?* and evaluate what it really means to surrender to Jesus.

2. **What do you think it means to "struggle" against sin?**

Having a new nature does not mean you will never sin again. True salvation involves turning from yourself and surrendering to Christ. Then—and only then—will His Spirit enter you. If His Spirit is alive in you, He will show Himself through you. If you have surrendered your will to Christ, you will *let* Him show Himself through your life.

This does not mean that a Christian can never sin. We still have the *capacity* to sin because our bodies have been *trained* to sin. But Scripture is clear: if you are truly God's child and you turn from Him to pursue sin, He will discipline you and bring you back onto the right path. If you sin and do not experience remorse and the correction of God, then you should consider if you are truly His child and have honestly given your heart to Him.

> If God doesn't discipline you as he does all of his children, it means that you are illegitimate and are not really his children at all. For our earthly fathers disciplined us for a few years, doing the best they knew how. But God's discipline is always good for us, so that we might share in his holiness. —**Hebrews 12:8, 10**

3. **What do you think it means for God to discipline you and bring to the right path?**

being a disciple of Jesus

Learning to live the way that Jesus desires us to is not always easy. Many people get discouraged and quit. Others continue to attend church and/or acknowledge God's existence, but completely ignore Christ's commands. This is a dangerously deceptive way to live. (Remember Christ's warning in Matthew 7:21)

Going through religious motions is not enough. You must learn to *passionately* follow Jesus.

> These people honor me with their lips, but their hearts are far from me. —**Matthew 15:8**

TRAINING VS TRYING

There is a big difference between trying and training. *Trying* usually entails doing what you have always done, only with more intensity. *Training* involves learning and developing better skills.

For example: If I were to promise $10,000 to anyone who could run a 5k race in under 20 minutes starting now, few could do it. No matter how hard they tried, most would come up short. However, if I were to say that in a year there will be a 5k race, with $10,000 awaiting those who finish in under 20 minutes, *and* I will provide a great trainer over the next year who has won *many* races—most of us would be a champion in a year if we participate in training.[23]

***Training* is the game-changer and the difference-maker.**

> Don't you realize that in a race everyone runs, but only one person gets the prize? So run to win! All athletes are disciplined in their training. They do it to win a prize that will fade away, but we do it for an eternal prize.

So I run with purpose in every step. I am not just shadowboxing. I discipline my body like an athlete, training it to do what it should. Otherwise, I fear that after preaching to others I myself might be disqualified.
—**1 Corinthians 9:24-27 NLT**

The Christian life is a life of training. The word disciple literally means, *someone who is trained*.[24] Disciples of Jesus are *people who are trained* in the ways of Jesus. Discipleship is the *process* of being trained in the ways of Jesus.

1. **Have you previously considered that the Christian life is a life of training?**

2. **Do you think that training to be a follower of Jesus, rather than just trying to do better, will be of more benefit to you spiritually? Why or why not?**

A TRAINING PLAN

As we have learned, the reborn child of God in you has new desires, but you have to learn to *recognize* and *develop* those new desires. Having a plan to implement discipleship in your life is a critical factor toward the success of your spiritual development.

> Good planning and hard work lead to
> prosperity, but hasty shortcuts lead to poverty.
> **—Proverbs 21:5 NLT**

This study can serve as your plan for spiritual growth and training. This book is the first in a series of six. By participating with the rest of this study, you will learn to make five more Core Decisions that will help you learn how to live in your created design as a child of God. These decisions will also help nurture the desires of your new nature (as discussed in *Day 28: New Creation—New Desires*).

You will learn to:

- Live in freedom from habitual patterns of sin
  – The Freedom Decision

- Develop an ongoing, passionate relationship with God
  – The Growth Decision

- View your human relationships the way God intended
  – The Relationships Decision

- Live your life engaged with Jesus' mission to bring the world to God. *– The Mission Decision*

- Align your life to move these concepts from intentions to priorities. *– The Alignment Decision*

> ...train yourself to be godly.
> **—1 Timothy 4:7b NLT**

3. What, if anything, prevents you from moving forward with this study?

TRAINING PARTNERS

It is recommended that you continue this study with a group of at least three or four other people. You are now part of God's family and need the strength that comes from family members. This will create a new spiritual culture for you to be part of and to integrate you into a spiritual family.

A study group should consist of a few people who are also learning for the first time, in addition to a few people who are further along in their spiritual journey. The insight and support that you give and receive will serve to spiritually strengthen all of you.

> Two are better than one, because they have a good return for their labor: If either of them falls down, one can help the other up. But pity anyone who falls and has no one to help him up. Also, if two lie down together, they will keep warm. But how can one keep warm alone? Though one may be overpowered, two can defend themselves. A cord of three strands is not quickly broken. —Ecclesiastes 4:9-12

For lack of guidance a nation falls, but victory is
won through many advisers. —**Proverbs 11:14**

4. **What, if anything, prevents you from joining with
    others on this journey?**

Congratulations! You have begun an amazing journey toward
discovering the life God created you to live!

WORKBOOK 1:

identity checkpoint

Before you move on to *Workbook 2: Freedom,* take a few minutes to evaluate your progress and the ways that you are applying the principles learned in this Workbook:

1. **Have you surrendered your life to the Lordship of Jesus and received the identity of a spiritually reborn child of God?**

2. **If you have surrendered your life to Jesus' Lordship, have you been baptized or made plans to be baptized? If yes, when? If not, what keeps you from doing so?**

3. Have you made plans to continue this study with others? If yes, with whom will you meet, and when will you meet next? If not, what keeps you from doing so?

4. If you have not surrendered your life to Jesus' Lordship, what factors keep you from doing so?

5. Which steps are you taking to further explore these factors?

notes

appendices

APPENDIX 1
substitute identities & scriptures

ACCOMPLISHMENTS

I am defined by what I can do or by what I know.

> Even youths grow tired and weary, and young men stumble and fall; but those who hope in the LORD will renew their strength. They will soar on wings like eagles; they will run and not grow weary, they will walk and not be faint.
> **—Isaiah 40:30**

> But whatever was to my profit I now consider loss for the sake of Christ. Yes, everything else is worthless when compared with the infinite value of knowing Christ Jesus my Lord. For his sake I have discarded everything else, counting it all as garbage, so that I could gain Christ.
> **—Philippians 3:7-8**

> Whatever you do, do your work heartily, as for the Lord rather than for men.
> **—Colossians 3:23 NASB**

ABILITIES

I am defined by a skill or ability that I have.

> You may say to yourself, "My power and the strength of my hands have produced this wealth for me." But remember the LORD your God, for it is he who gives you the ability to produce wealth, and so confirms his covenant, which he swore to your ancestors, as it is today.
> **—Deuteronomy 8:17-18**

For by the grace given me I say to every one of you: Do not think of yourself more highly than you ought, but rather think of yourself with sober judgment, in accordance with the faith God has distributed to each of you.
—**Romans 12:3**

Therefore, as the Scriptures say, "If you want to boast, boast only about the LORD."
—**1 Corinthians 1:31**

POSSESSIONS

I am defined by what I own.

Then he said to them, "Watch out! Be on your guard against all kinds of greed; a man's life does not consist in the abundance of his possessions." —**Luke 12:15**

Keep your lives free from the love of money and be content with what you have, because God has said, "Never will I leave you; never will I forsake you." —**Hebrews 13:5**

No one can serve two masters. Either he will hate the one and love the other, or he will be devoted to the one and despise the other. You cannot serve both God and Money.
—**Matthew 6:24**

Therefore I tell you, do not worry about your life, what you will eat or drink; or about your body, what you will wear. Is not life more important than food, and the body more important than clothes? —**Matthew 6:25**

APPEARANCE

I am defined by how I look.

Charm is deceptive, and beauty is fleeting; but a woman who fears the LORD is to be praised. —**Proverbs 31:30**

For women who claim to be devoted to God should make themselves attractive by the good things they do. —**1 Timothy 2:10 NLT**

APPROVAL

I am defined by who accepts me.

I'm not interested in crowd approval. And do you know why? Because I know you and your crowds. I know that love, especially God's love, is not on your working agenda.
—**John 5:41-42 The Message**

Peter and the other apostles replied: "We must obey God rather than men! —**Acts 5:29**

Am I now trying to win the approval of human beings, or of God ? Or am I trying to please people? If I were still trying to please people, I would not be a servant of Christ.
—**Galatians 1:10**

On the contrary, we speak as men approved by God to be entrusted with the gospel. We are not trying to please men but God, who tests our hearts. —**1 Thessalonians 2:4**

We were not looking for praise from people, not from you or anyone else, even though as apostles of Christ we could have asserted our authority. —**1 Thessalonians 2:6**

 Blessed are you when people insult you, persecute you and falsely say all kinds of evil against you because of me. Rejoice and be glad, because great is your reward in heaven, for in the same way they persecuted the prophets who were before you. —**Matthew 5:11-12**

AFFECTION

I am defined by who loves me.

...all things (including you) have been created through him (Jesus) and for him (Jesus).
—**Colossians 1:16b**

The Lord appeared to us in the past, saying: "I have loved you with an everlasting love; I have drawn you with unfailing kindness.
—**Jeremiah 31:3**

For I am convinced that neither death nor life, neither angels nor demons, neither the present nor the future, nor any powers, neither height nor depth, nor anything else in all creation, will be able to separate us from the love of God that is in Christ Jesus our Lord. —**Romans 8:38-39**

ATTENTION

I am defined by being noticed for positive or negative behavior, or by getting sympathy from others.

> How can you believe since you accept glory from one another but do not seek the glory that comes from the only God? —**John 5:44**

> Do nothing out of selfish ambition or vain conceit. Rather, in humility value others above yourselves. —**Phillipians 2:3**

> Be careful not to practice your righteousness in front of others to be seen by them. If you do, you will have no reward from your Father in heaven. —**Matthew 6:1**

POWER

I am defined by being in control.

> Son of man, say to the ruler of Tyre, "This is what the Sovereign LORD says: In the pride of your heart you say, "I am a god; I sit on the throne of a god in the heart of the seas.' But you are a man and not a god, though you think you are as wise as a god." —**Ezekiel 28:2**

> Trust in the LORD with all your heart and lean not on your own understanding; in all your ways submit to him, and he will make your paths straight. —**Proverbs 3:5-6**

> Look to the LORD and his strength; seek his face always. —**1 Chronicles 16:11**

> "Not by might nor by power but by my Spirit" says the Lord God Almighty. —**Zechariah 4:6**

There is no one holy like the LORD; there is no
one besides you; there is no Rock like our God.
—**1 Samuel 2:2**

APPETITIES

I am defined by my desires. These can be natural desires such
as those of food or sex, or acquired desires such as those for
drugs and alcohol.

Appetite for food

"My food," said Jesus, "is to do the will of him
who sent me and to finish his work."
—**John 4:34**

I know what it is to be in need, and I know
what it is to have plenty. I have learned the
secret of being content in any and every
situation, whether well fed or hungry, whether
living in plenty or in want. I can do everything
through him who gives me strength.
—**Philippians 4:12-13**

Their destiny is destruction, their god is their
stomach, and their glory is in their shame. Their
mind is on earthly things. —**Philippians 3:19**

Sexual appetite

"....How then could I do such a wicked thing
and sin against God?" (Joseph's response to
sexual temptation.) —**Genesis 39:9b**

Flee from sexual immorality. All other sins
a person commits are outside the body, but
whoever sins sexually, sins against their own
body. Do you not know that your bodies are
temples of the Holy Spirit, who is in you, whom

you have received from God? You are not your own; you were bought at a price. Therefore honor God with your bodies.
—**1 Corinthians 6:18-20**

Appetite for alcohol or other drugs.

Do not get drunk on wine, which leads to debauchery. Instead, be filled with the Spirit.
—**Ephesians 5:18**

Wine is a mocker and beer a brawler; whoever is led astray by them is not wise.
—**Proverbs 20:1**

PLEASURE

I am defined by being comfortable and feeling good.

But he will pour out his anger and wrath on those who live for themselves, who refuse to obey the truth and instead live lives of wickedness. —**Romans 2:8**

And I'll say to myself, "You have plenty of grain laid up for many years. Take life easy; eat, drink and be merry." But God said to him, "You fool! This very night your life will be demanded from you. Then who will get what you have prepared for yourself?"
—**Luke 12:19-20**

APPENDIX 2

essential christian beliefs

There are some questions about God and faith that no one can answer for certain; but many of these questions are not about essential beliefs for obtaining salvation. Following are a few essential beliefs that are important for salvation.[25]

GOD EXISTS AND HE CREATED EVERYTHING FOR HIS PURPOSE.

Many argue that because God is unseen, He must not exist, therefore it is naive to believe He could have designed and formed the Universe. It is true that faith in something that is unseen is required in order to believe that God created the Universe.

> By faith we understand that the entire universe was formed at God's command, that what we now see did not come from anything that can be seen. —**Hebrews 11:3 NLT**

However, it is also true that to believe that the Universe came through a random string of events *also requires faith in something unseen*. Because no one was present to witness how the Universe came to be, both positions require belief or trust in something that cannot be physically verified.

Which one actually makes more sense to believe? That a Creator designed and formed the Universe, or that the Universe was constructed through random chance? Which view requires the most trust in an unlikely explanation?

The verifiable physical laws of science indicate that things do not naturally become better. If left to themselves, things fall into disarray—they do not randomly fall into order or structure.

Based on this natural tendency for things to fall into disarray, what are the odds that the Universe and *every complex, ordered organism in it,* came into existence through random chance? It is more likely that a tornado can blow through a lumberyard and produce an immaculately constructed house than that a universe such as ours could be formed through random events.

When we observe the intricate order and detail in even the most basic units of matter, it makes sense to believe that there is a design and a Designer behind it all. The order and structure of the Universe itself indicate that God exists.

> For ever since the world was created, people have seen the earth and sky. Through everything God made, they can clearly see his invisible qualities—his eternal power and divine nature. So they have no excuse for not knowing God. **—Romans 1:20 NLT**

Does God exist? Did He design and form the Universe? The evidence suggests that *He does and He did!* This is a more logical conclusion than the belief that everything exists by random chance. The exact processes that God used to produce the Universe are not as important to understand as is the belief that God *did* design and create it all.

JESUS IS WHO HE SAID HE IS—GOD IN THE FLESH SENT TO REDEEM HUMANITY.

The first disciples believed Jesus' resurrection proved that He is who He said He is—God in the flesh sent to redeem humanity. His resurrection proves that He is Lord of all things—including death. Scripture makes this belief about Jesus an essential requirement for salvation from sin.

> If you declare with your mouth, "Jesus is Lord," and believe in your heart that God raised him from the dead, you will be saved.
> **—Romans 10:9**

Naturally, there are many questions concerning Jesus' death and resurrection. *Did He really die, or just faint? Did His disciples steal His body and then lie about His resurrection?*

Many of these questions are addressed and verified, or discounted in historical accounts. We were not there to witness these events, but Scripture writers noted hundreds of witnesses who were.

> He was seen by Peter and then by the Twelve.
> After that, he was seen by more than 500 of his
> followers at one time, most of whom are still
> alive, though some have died.
> **—1 Corinthians 15:5-6**

When this was written, most of the witnesses could be found and questioned. What is the likelihood of 500 people agreeing to something they did not see? Many were killed for insisting that Jesus Christ was resurrected. Hundreds will not die for something they *know* is a lie; the pressure would cause someone to crack.

It has been suggested that the witnesses were hallucinating. Again, what is the likelihood that 500 people experienced the *same* hallucination and would be willing to die for it?

The truth is, hundreds of people saw Christ walking around alive, eating and talking after He was killed and resurrected. This many eyewitness accounts would stand up in any court of law. However, the biggest evidence of His resurrection is the way their lives were altered after experiencing His Presence.

THE BIBLE IS RELIABLE AND VALID.

To say the Bible is reliable means that what we read today is what the writers recorded.[26]

Because none of the original texts of the Bible exist, all translators use copies of the original texts. Some insist that the texts have been so tampered with it is impossible to know what was written. A thorough scientific investigation disproves this claim.

Minor copying errors may be found from one manuscript to another, but these are easily caught by the trained eye. When manuscripts older than those used for our current translations of the

Bible were discovered, examined and compared, very few copy errors were found.

The evidence is strong that what we currently read is reliably close to what was originally written and intended. We read them in a translated language because Greek, Hebrew and Aramaic—the original languages the Bible was written in—are now dead. No culture currently communicates with them. (We will learn more about Biblical translations in *Workbook 3: Growth*)

To say the Bible is valid means that the Bible is true. It is what it claims to be and its message can be trusted. Through the inspiration of God, the writers recounted incidents that they witnessed, and gave instruction from God. In other words, they were not making up or lying about what they wrote.

Some accuse Bible writers of not properly recording details, insisting that the books of the Bible were written too many years after their recorded events to be accurate and trustworthy. However, most of the recorded events in the Bible were recorded soon after they occurred.

Although several other ancient historical narratives were written hundreds of years after events transpired, some critics give these other narratives more historical weight than the accounts of Scripture that were written soon after their recorded events. This is a hypocritical standard.

People also accuse Biblical writers of a conspiracy to manipulate people. But as mentioned, it is unlikely that so many people would be willing to die for something they *knew* was a lie.

Furthermore, the Bible was written over the span of thousands of years, by more than 40 authors with different backgrounds and styles. When you see their consistent theme and message, you see evidence of the Divine Author, God, expressing Himself through human writers.

Remember to seek to know God while you seek answers to your questions.

> You will seek me and find me when you seek me with all your heart. —**Jeremiah 29:13**

God's promises for His children

....

YOU ARE NOW GOD'S CHILD
AND PART OF HIS FAMILY!

....

Yet to all who did receive him, to those who believed in his name, he gave the right to become children of God. —**John 1:12**

Both the one who makes people holy and those who are made holy are of the same family. So Jesus is not ashamed to call them brothers and sisters. —**Hebrews 2:11**

He predestined us for adoption to sonship through Jesus Christ, in accordance with his pleasure and will. —**Ephesians 1:5**

Consequently, you are no longer foreigners and strangers, but fellow citizens with God's people and also members of his household.
—**Ephesians 2:19**

But we are citizens of heaven, where the Lord Jesus Christ lives. And we are eagerly waiting for him to return as our Savior.
—**Philippians 3:20**

Now if we are children, then we are heirs— heirs of God and co-heirs with Christ, if indeed we share in his sufferings in order that we may also share in his glory. —**Romans 8:17**

CHRIST LOVES YOU AND NOTHING CAN EVER SEPARATE YOU FROM HIS LOVE.

The Lord appeared to us in the past, saying: "I have loved you with an everlasting love; I have drawn you with unfailing kindness."
—**Jeremiah 31:3**

I give them eternal life, and they shall never perish; no one will snatch them out of my hand.
—**John 10:28**

For I am convinced that neither death nor life, neither angels nor demons, neither the present nor the future, nor any powers, neither height nor depth, nor anything else in all creation, will be able to separate us from the love of God that is in Christ Jesus our Lord. —**Romans 8:38-39**

YOU HAVE BEEN FORGIVEN OF ALL YOUR SINS AND ARE NOW THE RIGHTEOUSNESS OF GOD.

When you were dead in your sins and in the uncircumcision of your flesh, God made you alive with Christ. He forgave us all our sins.
—**Colossians 2:13**

God made him who had no sin to be sin for us, so that in him we might become the righteousness of God. —**2 Corinthians 5:21**

YOU ARE NOW HOLY, BLAMELESS AND FREE FROM ALL CONDEMNATION. YOUR PAST ROLES, FAILURES, STRUGGLES AND PAIN NO LONGER DEFINE YOU.

But now he has reconciled you by Christ's physical body through death to present you holy in his sight, without blemish and free from accusation. —**Colossians 1:22**

For he chose us in him before the creation of the world to be holy and blameless in his sight…
—**Ephesians 1:4**

Therefore, there is now no condemnation for those who are in Christ Jesus. —**Romans 8:1**

YOU HAVE BEEN CRUCIFIED WITH CHRIST, RAISED AGAIN WITH CHRIST AND HAVE HIS DIVINE NATURE. YOU ARE A NEW PERSON.

I have been crucified with Christ and I no longer live, but Christ lives in me. The life I now live in the body, I live by faith in the Son of God, who loved me and gave himself for me.
—**Galatians 2:20**

We were therefore buried with him through baptism into death in order that, just as Christ was raised from the dead through the glory of the Father, we too may live a new life.
—**Romans 6:4**

Through these he has given us his very great and precious promises, so that through them you may participate in the divine nature, having escaped the corruption in the world caused by evil desires. —**2 Peter 1:4**

This means that anyone who belongs to Christ has become a new person. The old life is gone; a new life has begun! —**2 Corinthians 5:17 NLT**

YOU ARE THE TEMPLE OF GOD.

What agreement is there between the temple of God and idols? For we are the temple of the living God. As God has said: "I will live with them and walk among them, and I will be their God, and they will be my people."
—**2 Corinthians 6:16**

And if the Spirit of him who raised Jesus from the dead is living in you, he who raised Christ from the dead will also give life to your mortal bodies because of his Spirit who lives in you.
—**Romans 8:11**

YOU ARE ACCEPTED IN CHRIST AND ARE NOW RECONCILED TO GOD. YOU HAVE PEACE WITH GOD.

Accept one another, then, just as Christ accepted you, in order to bring praise to God.
—**Romans 15:7**

For if, while we were God's enemies, we were reconciled to him through the death of his Son, how much more, having been reconciled, shall we be saved through his life! —**Romans 5:10**

Therefore, since we have been justified through faith, we have peace with God through our Lord Jesus Christ. —**Romans 5:1**

YOU HAVE BEEN DELIVERED FROM THE POWER OF DARKNESS AND ARE SEATED WITH CHRIST IN HEAVENLY REALMS. YOU ARE A KING AND A PRIEST OF GOD.

For he has rescued us from the dominion of darkness and brought us into the kingdom of the Son he loves. —**Colossians 1:13**

And God raised us up with Christ and seated us with him in the heavenly realms in Christ Jesus. —**Ephesians 2:6**

...and has made us to be a kingdom and priests to serve his God and Father—to him be glory and power for ever and ever! Amen. —**Revelation 1:6**

YOU HAVE OVERCOME THE WORLD AND WILL ALWAYS TRIUMPH IN CHRIST.

I have told you these things, so that in me you may have peace. In this world you will have trouble. But take heart! I have overcome the world. —**John 16:33**

But thanks be to God, who always leads us as captives in Christ's triumphal procession and uses us to spread the aroma of the knowledge of him everywhere. —**2 Corinthians 2:14**

Go back and place a mark beside every promise that stands out to you.

ENDNOTES

[1] Beginning a discipleship course by addressing man's search for meaning is not a novel concept. The most popular example would be: Warren, Rick. *The Purpose Driven Life: What on Earth Am I Here for?* Grand Rapids, MI: Zondervan, 2007.

[2] These three (3) focuses of discipleship have been made popular by many Christian authors and teachers. A notable example is: Rainer, Thom S., and Eric Geiger. Simple Church: Returning to Gods Process for Making Disciples. Nashville, TN: B & H Pub. Group, 2011.

[3] This is adapted from the Westminster Shorter Catechism, developed in 1646-1647. A catechism is a summary of Christian doctrines, taught in question and answer format. Refer to: http://www.shortercatechism.com/resources/wsc/wsc_001.html

[4] These needs are *loosely* influenced by what is traditionally known as Maslow's hierarchy of needs, a theory of psychological health that teaches a priority of needs that begins with basic needs, moves to psychological needs and culminates with self-fulfillment. Based on a life-time of pastoral work, the author sees these needs as the driving force behind most human decisions.

[5] This list of Substitute Identities was developed over time. It was initially inspired by concepts presented in: Breen, Mike. "An Obituary for the American Church." Verge. http://www.vergenetwork.org/2012/02/02/obituary-for-the-american-church-mike-breen/

[6] Ecclesiastes 2:11

[7] Luke 19:10

[8] As a Christian, God's Word—not people's opinions, our culture or our family's traditions—must determine our moral compass. This study will focus on the moral code of God outlined in the following New Testament passages: Galatians 5:19-21; Ephesians 5:3-5; Colossians 3:5; 1 Corinthians 6:9-10; Revelations 21:8; Romans 1:29-32. These passages outline thoughts and behaviors called sinful works or deeds of the flesh. The warning is repeatedly clear that if we do not turn from these things, we will not inherit the kingdom of God.

[9] https://www.biblestudytools.com/lexicons/greek/nas/hamartia.html

[10] For a complete English text of the Apostle and Nicene Creeds (the Ancient Creeds of the Christian faith) refer to: https://www.christianitytoday.com/biblestudies/articles/churchhomeleadership/nicene-apostles-creeds.html

[11] The reason for Jesus' death has been analyzed by Christians throughout history. Different traditions emphasize different aspects. The following book demonstrates this as the authors analyze four different views of the Atonement of Christ: Eddy, Paul R. and James K. Beilby *The Nature of Atonement: Four Views.* Downer Grove, Il. IVP Academie, 2006. (The author is not advo-

cating for every view presented in this book, but it bears mentioning Jesus' death has been viewed from different perceptives in Christian history. The truth is, due to the immense gravity of its impact, we may never fully grasp the complete significance, weight and importance of Jesus' death, burial and resurrection to humanity.)

[12] Keller, Timothy. *The Reason for God: Belief in an Age of Skepticism*. Penguin, 2016. Pg. 185-188.

[13] https://www.blueletterbible.org/lang/lexicon/lexicon.cfm?Strongs=G5547&t=KJV

[14] Lewis, C. S. (Clive Staples). *Mere Christianity*. New York: Walker &, 1987. Chapter 3.

[15] The Wesley Center Online. "The Sermons of John Wesley – Sermon 1: Salvation by Faith." wesley.nnu.edu. http://wesley.nnu.edu/john-wesley/the-sermons-of-john-wesley-1872-edition/sermon-1-salvation-by-faith

[16] This list of Incomplete Beliefs was inspired by John Wesley's sermon, Salvation by Faith. Ibid.

[17] The author does not take credit for this analogy but cannot locate its origin. Variations of this example have circulated in Christian thought for some time.

[18] https://www.blueletterbible.org/lang/lexicon/lexicon.cfm?Strongs=G3340&t=KJV

[19] Strobel, Lee, *The Case for Faith: A Journalist Investigates the Toughest Objections to Christianity*. Grand Rapids, MI: Zondervan.com, 2000. Pg. 223-262. Also reference Ortberg, John. *Faith & Doubt*. Grand Rapids, MI: Zondervan, 2008.

[20] Baker, John and Richard D. Warren. *Life's Healing Choices: Freedom from Your Hurts, Hang-ups, and Habits*. New York, NY: Howard Books., 2007. Pg. 13-35

[21] The origin of this quote is from an acquaintance the author knew many years ago. (The author cannot locate him or remember his last name, but his first name is Dallas.)

[22] Wiersbe, Warren W, *The Weirsbe Bible Commentary: New Testament*. Colorado Springs, CO, 2007. Pg. 237

[23] Ortberg, John, *The Life You've Always Wanted*. Grand Rapids, MI: Zondervan, 2002. Pg. 40-44 (Kindle Edition). Also see Ortberg, John, Laurie Pederson, and Judson Poling. *Growth: Training vs. Trying*. Grand Rapids, MI: Zondervan, 2000.

[24] The word disciple comes from the Latin word *discere*. The word discipline is also derived from this word. It means to *learn*, or practically it means *to be taught or trained*. Thus, we conclude that a disciple is literally one who is disciplined or trained. http://latindictionary.wikidot.com/verb:discere

[25] The author does not take credit for the examples used in this section. Variations of these examples have circulated in Christian thought for some time. For further study consider the following books: Strobel, Lee. *The Case for Christ: A Journalist's Personal Investigation of the Evidence for Jesus.* Grand Rapids, MI: Zondervan.com, 2016, and Strobel, Lee. *The Case for Faith: A Journalist Investigates the Toughest Objections to Christianity.* Grand Rapids, MI: Zondervan.com, 2000.

[26] Go to the following website for more information and resources to support the validity and reliability of the Bible. https://www.truelife.org/answers/why-believe-the-bible-9b49ac25-c1c6-4e9c-92ee-095ea3fe1182

Workbook 1: Identity Checkpoint —Icons made by Roundicons from Flaticon is licensed by Creative Commons BY 3.0

notes

Discover Discipleship Course

1. IDENTITY

2. FREEDOM

3. GROWTH

4. RELATIONSHIPS

5. MISSION

6. ALIGNMENT

For purchasing information and bulk discounts
go to discoverdiscipleship.com